Yoga Nidra Scripts

Praise for

Yoga Nidra Scripts: 22 Meditations for Effortless Relaxation, Rejuvenation and Reconnection
Tamara Verma *(Tamara Skyhawk)*

"So good, and timely... a roadmap to inner reconnection and enlightenment... a must-have resource for yoga teachers and healing practitioners, and one I keep reaching for."

– Ashley Petrovsky, RYT 500, Ash Sky Yoga

"*Yoga Nidra Scripts* is a valuable teaching tool for yoga teachers, practitioners, healers and others who guide Yoga Nidras. Tamara Skyhawk offers a rich and varied assortment of eloquently written scripts to guide others on a deeply relaxing and healing Yoga Nidra journey. These Yoga Nidra scripts are accessible to modern practitioners yet drawn from time-honored lineages that have refined this profound meditation technique."

– Aiyana Athenian, Co-Founder of ShivaShakti School of Yoga

"I got rave reviews with the scripts! ... I highly recommend *Yoga Nidra Scripts* for anyone teaching yoga, mindfulness, or looking to deepen their own connection to the practice of Yoga Nidra. Tamara Skyhawk has put together a valuable resource with easy to follow scripts you can plug into your classes. With all the script choices, you're sure to find just the right one for your theme and timeframe. I've been teaching yoga for many years, and feel confident that these scripts will be useful for many more years to come."

– Aruna Kathy Humphrys, Lead Trainer at Young Yoga Masters
and Ambassador Yoga

Yoga Nidra Scripts

22 Meditations for Effortless Relaxation, Rejuvenation and Reconnection

Tamara Verma
(Tamara Skyhawk)

Deep gratitude to Aiyana and Krishna
of ShivaShakti School of Yoga for reigniting my passion for
Yoga Nidra with their thoughtful, beautiful teachings.

Disclaimer

This book is not intended to treat, heal or prescribe. The information contained herein is in no way to be considered as a substitute for a consultation with a duly licensed health care professional.

Author: Tamara Verma *(Tamara Skyhawk)*

Copyright © 2020 by Tamara Verma *(Tamara Skyhawk)*

First Edition 2020

Publisher: RTV Yoga Inc.

ISBN: 978-1-7774888-0-2 (paperback) 978-1-7774888-1-9 (e-book)

Contents

Author's Note

Over 20 years of teaching yoga, I've noticed a general shift in people, their lifestyles and needs. I believe, as a result, there's been a change in which yogic practices are most relevant right now.

I've seen people waking up to the fact that a "yoga body" is not the key to happiness. I also see people completely depleted on all fronts: physically, mentally and spiritually. What I believe people need more than anything now is *rest*.

One of the yogic practices that fills this need for rest and rejuvenation is Yoga Nidra – sleep with trace awareness. It also happens to be one of the most effortless and deliciously enjoyable yoga practices.

What's more, in addition to rest and rejuvenation, Yoga Nidra offers the other "r" word people need right now – reconnection. I see people less connected to themselves than ever before. Disconnected from their bodies, energies, minds, inner wisdom – never mind their higher selves.

I created these Yoga Nidra scripts so you and I can guide people to relax, rejuvenate, and also reconnect with, or even discover for the first time, their full spectrum of being: living body, energetic being, well of inner knowing, and Source itself.

There is a lot of healing to be had. And oh, the sweetness of doing nothing. Doing nothing and gaining everything – that is the gift of Yoga Nidra.

About This Book

There are a variety of scripts in this book – different lengths, different purposes, for different times and seasons, including elements from different lineages and styles.

However, there are a few things the scripts share in common. In my experience, familiarity helps the mind rest. When you have a basic sense of what's coming next in your Yoga Nidra practice, there's less need to think or anticipate, so the mind settles. That is so key to an effective Yoga Nidra practice. In this book, I've used a consistent script structure and common phrases to create familiarity for more effortless relaxation.

I find what works best for me and the people I guide is using similar structure, phrases and techniques and once in a while shaking it up with something new. That way the familiar patterns don't become wallpaper to the point where the mind just ignores and wanders off to thoughts of dinner or weekend plans.

I've also tried to keep language simple and familiar. These are not scripts only for seasoned yogis. I wanted to make them feel accessible for anyone. For that reason, I've often used simple terms such as "energy", rather than "prana", or "navel centre" rather than "Manipura chakra", and so on. If you're leading a group of yogis, feel free to use the Sanskrit words.

I've given approximate timings for the scripts, as well as suggested pre- and post-practices to help you plan your sessions. Timings will depend on your reading pace, but for general guidance, a line break indicates a brief pause, '(pause)' indicates a pause for one deep breath and '(long pause)' indicates a break for three deep breaths. As always, "read the room" and adjust pacing and flow accordingly.

Hear samples of the pacing I use with these

FREE audio recordings:

• Anytime Calming

• Overflowing Heart Yoga Nidra

• Rainbow Light Yoga Nidra

Get them at tamaraskyhawk.com/free

Finally, I've tried to make the language of the scripts inclusive for all people whether or not they are able or comfortable to lie in savasana. The options to sit supported or lie in an alternate position are also included.

Tips for Using This Book

These scripts are meant as a starting point. If creativity doesn't come easily for you, then by all means read them as-is and simply adjust as you observe and speak with your practitioners.

If you *are* creative, access your inner wisdom and play. Edit to your own voice, omit sections or add elements to suit the needs of your practitioners. Even I don't read these scripts the same way twice!

Always be responsive to the people you're guiding. Ask yourself, what is appropriate for this space, with these people, at this time? And ask them as well.

Give a bit of a primer before leading each session. For example, if you plan to lead the Floating Leaf Yoga Nidra, ask if everyone present is comfortable with that. You might learn that someone has a fear of drowning, so that script won't be appropriate. Don't be afraid to ask, adjust and always have a backup plan.

Also, continue to adapt as the people you're guiding grow in their practice and as you grow in your ability as a guide. In general, the shorter scripts are a good way to introduce the practice of Yoga Nidra, and the longer scripts are for people who are already experienced.

I've included suggested pre- and post-practices such as yoga poses, mudras and mantras to give you the ability to craft fuller, more profound Yoga Nidra sessions. The suggestions are primarily for teachers familiar with asanas, mudras and mantras. If you aren't familiar, at least it's a starting point for an Internet search, or you could consider my Mudra Yoga Teacher Training for full detail on mudras. (More information at tamaraskyhawk.com.)

Wishing you and all the people you share these scripts with much joyful relaxation, rejuvenation and reconnection!

Anytime Calming *(15 min.)*

A quick, soothing practice to calm you anytime.

Suggested Pre- and Post-Practices:

- Use before or after a yoga class or other healing treatment. Or if using as a standalone practice, consider beginning with a minute or two of simple stretches to release bodily tension – such as seated or standing shoulder rolls, twist, side bend and forward fold.

- Prepare or finish with the soothing, universal mantra of Om

Settling

Getting comfortable, lying down or sitting, supported. Choosing any position that's comfortable right now. Getting ready for this practice of calming.

Tucking a thin pillow or blanket under your head if you like.

Cover yourself with a blanket if you like.

Doing anything you need to do to get as comfortable as possible. (long pause)

Check for any lumps or bumps of clothing, jewellery, or anything else that might distract you. If you find any, adjust them now. (pause)

Scan your whole body, making sure you're as comfortable as can be. Feet relaxed... legs... hips... back... arms... shoulders... jaw... forehead. Checking in and making any further adjustments if it will help you be your most comfortable. (pause)

Feel yourself settling in.

Serene, like a still lake. (pause)

And now, setting aside anything that's happened before this moment.

Setting aside anything that's happening after this practice.

Bring all of your awareness into your practice for the next 15 minutes.

Setting everything aside for these moments to calm and connect.

Take a deep breath in... and as you exhale, letting go of any thoughts you'd like to let go of in this moment.

Let go of any thoughts. Let go of any need to do. Just being.

This is your time for yourself.

No agenda. Just peace. (pause)

Make any final adjustments if you haven't already. (pause)

Begin to experience the stillness even more. Know that you can move, but if it feels good, allow yourself to enjoy this stillness. This chance to do *nothing*.

Resting. Just as you like.

If it feels restful, allow these words to be received energetically, rather than mentally. Even the mind can rest now.

In its place, there is effortless awareness. (pause)

Feel all experience becoming more and more effortless.

Serene and effortless. (pause)

Yoga Nidra has now begun. (pause)

Rotation of Consciousness

A series of energetic points will be named.

Allow awareness to float effortlessly from point to point.

Start by floating awareness to the point between the eyebrows

Effortless awareness of the point between the eyebrows

The hollow of the throat

The right shoulder joint

Moving freely to the right elbow joint

Wrist joint

The right thumb

The tip of the index finger

Tip of the middle finger

Tip of the ring finger

Tip of the little finger

Effortless awareness

The right wrist joint

Elbow joint

Shoulder joint

Hollow of the throat

Shifting awareness over to the left shoulder joint

Elbow joint

Wrist joint

The left thumb

Tip of the index finger

Tip of the middle finger

Tip of the ring finger

Tip of the little finger

Shifting freely

The left wrist joint

Elbow joint

Shoulder joint

Hollow of the throat

The heart centre

The right side of the chest

The heart centre

The left side of the chest

The heart centre

The heart centre

The heart centre

Resting awareness at the heart centre. Not thinking, just feeling. (pause)

Breath Awareness

Become aware of the breath.

Aware of the body gently moving with each inhale and exhale. (pause)

Notice on the inhalation that the abdomen gently rises, then chest rises.

And on the exhalation, abdomen falls, chest falls.

Inhale abdomen rises, chest rises.

Exhale abdomen falls, chest falls.

Feel this wave of breath.

Like a wave washing into the shore, then washing away from the shore.

Follow this gentle wave of breath.

Each breath, watching the wave rise, and watching it fall.

No need to make any changes to the breath.

Simply watching.

Watching the natural wave of breath, like watching gentle waves on the ocean.

Begin to count the waves.

Simply follow the natural pace of breath.

Inhale 1

Exhale 2

Inhale 3

Exhale 4

And so on, up to 26.

If you lose track that's fine. Simply start again at 1. (pause for 1 minute)

Now let go of counting the waves of breath.

It doesn't matter if you reached twenty-six or lost track.

Letting go of the count.

Externalization

Bring your awareness back to your heart centre. (pause)

Notice the heart centre rising on inhalation, falling on exhalation. (pause)

Bring awareness back to your body.

Yoga Nidra is now complete. (pause)

Feel your body peacefully resting. (pause)

Feel the support beneath you. (pause)

Notice the temperature of the space you're in. (pause)

Notice the sounds. (pause)

Introduce more movement in the body by taking a few deep breaths. (pause)

Now wiggle your fingers and toes. Feel the lightness of the sensation.

Stretch or move your body in any way you like. (pause)

And if you're lying down, when you're ready, roll to your right side. Take a few deep breaths here. Taking with you any calming sensation from your practice today. (pause)

If you were lying down, slowly, gently press yourself up to sitting, keep your eyes closed if you can, and take a deep breath.

We'll finish by chanting Om and Shanti. Om is a universal vibration. Shanti means peace.

Om, Om, Om, (can continue for a few minutes) Shanti, Shanti, Shanti (pause)

When you're ready, softly open your eyes and bring the calming sensation into the room and into the rest of your day.

Anytime Rejuvenation *(15 min.)*

If you're feeling dull or stuck, this is a quick practice for rejuvenating.

<u>Suggested Pre- and Post-Practices:</u>

- Use before or after a yoga class or other healing treatment. Or if using as a standalone practice, consider beginning with a minute or two of simple stretches to release bodily tension – such as seated or standing shoulder rolls, twist, side bend and forward fold.

- Prepare with a few minutes of Prana Mudra for harnessing energy.

Settling

Getting comfortable, lying down or sitting, supported.

Choosing any position that's comfortable right now. Getting ready for this practice for rejuvenation.

Tucking a thin pillow or blanket under your head if you like.

Cover yourself with a blanket if you like.

Doing anything you need to do to get as comfortable as possible. (long pause)

Check for any lumps or bumps of clothing, jewellery, or anything else that might distract you.

If you find any, adjust them now. (pause)

Scan your whole body, making sure you're as comfortable as can be. Feet relaxed… legs… hips… back… arms… shoulders… jaw… forehead. Checking in and making any further adjustments if it will help you be your most comfortable. (pause)

Feel yourself settling in. (pause)

And now, setting aside anything that's happened before this moment.

Setting aside anything that's happening after this practice.

Bring all of your awareness into your practice for the next 15 minutes.

Setting everything aside for these moments to rejuvenate. (pause)

Take a deep breath in… and as you exhale, letting go of any tension, any fatigue.

Let go of any thoughts, any need to do. Just being.

This is your time for yourself.

Nothing to accomplish. Just enjoying peace. (pause)

Make any final adjustments if you haven't already. (pause)

Begin to experience the stillness even more. Know that you can move, but if it feels good, allow yourself to enjoy this stillness. This chance to do nothing.

Resting. Just as you like.

If it feels restful, allow these words to be received energetically, rather than mentally. Even the mind can rest now.

In its place, there is effortless awareness. (pause)

Feel all experience becoming more and more effortless.

Serene and effortless. (pause)

Yoga Nidra has now begun. (pause)

Rotation of Consciousness

A series of energetic points will be named.

Allow awareness to flow freely from point to point.

Like connecting points of light or energy currents.

Start with awareness on the point between the eyebrows

Experiencing energetically, rather than physically.

The point between the eyebrows

The hollow of the throat

The right shoulder joint

Shifting freely

The right elbow joint

Wrist joint

The right thumb

The tip of the index finger

Tip of the middle finger

Tip of the ring finger

Tip of the little finger

Experiencing energetically

The right wrist joint

Elbow joint

Shoulder joint

Hollow of the throat

Over to the left shoulder joint

Elbow joint

Wrist joint

The left thumb

Tip of the index finger

Tip of the middle finger

Tip of the ring finger

Tip of the little finger

Back up to the left wrist joint

Elbow joint

Shoulder joint

Hollow of the throat

The heart centre

The right side of the chest

The heart centre

The left side of the chest

The heart centre

The navel centre

Tip of the tailbone

The right hip joint

Right knee joint

Ankle joint

The right big toe

Tip of the second toe

Tip of the third toe

Tip of the fourth toe

Tip of the baby toe

Back up to the right ankle joint

Knee joint

Hip joint

Tip of the tailbone

Sweeping awareness to the left hip joint

Left knee joint

Ankle joint

The left big toe

Tip of the second toe

Tip of the third toe

Tip of the fourth toe

Tip of the baby toe

Back up to the left ankle joint

Knee joint

Hip joint

Tip of the tailbone

The navel centre

The heart centre

Hollow of the throat

The eyebrow centre

The eyebrow centre

The eyebrow centre (pause)

Breath Awareness

Now become aware of the breath.

No need to change the breath in any way, simply bring awareness to the breath.

As you exhale, feel that you let go of any fatigue, stress, tension.

As you inhale, feel that you're pulling in *boundless energy*.

Exhale letting go of fatigue, stress, tension.

Inhale filling up with boundless energy.

Exhale from the crown of the head down to the toes.

Inhale from the toes up to the crown of the head.

Exhale from the crown of the head down to the ankles.

Inhale from the ankles up to the crown of the head.

Exhale from the crown of the head down to the knees.

Inhale from the knees up to the crown of the head.

Exhale from the crown down the spine to the tailbone.

Inhale from the tailbone up the spine to the crown.

Exhale from the crown down the spine to the navel.

Inhale from the navel up the spine to the crown.

Exhale from the crown down the spine to the heart centre.

Inhale from the heart centre up the spine to the crown.

Exhale from the crown down to the throat centre.

Inhale from the throat centre up the spine to the crown.

Exhale from the crown down to the bridge between the nostrils.

Inhale from the bridge between the nostrils up to the crown.

Now to the third eye, exhale down to the bridge between the nostrils.

Inhale from the bridge between the nostrils, up to the third eye.

Back to the crown, exhale down to the bridge between the nostrils.

Inhale from the bridge between the nostrils up to the crown.

Exhale from the crown down the spine to the throat centre.

Inhale from the throat centre up the spine to the crown.

Exhale from the crown down the spine to the heart centre.

Inhale from the heart centre up the spine to the crown.

Exhale from the crown down the spine to the navel.

Inhale from the navel up the spine to the crown.

Exhale from the crown down the spine to the tailbone.

Inhale from the tailbone up the spine to the crown.

Exhale from the crown of the head down to the knees.

Inhale from the knees up to the crown of the head.

Exhale from the crown of the head down to the ankles.

Inhale from the ankles up to the crown of the head.

Exhale from the crown of head down to the toes.

Inhale from the toes up to the crown of the head. (pause)

Feel that the whole body is breathing in and out. (pause)

Inhaling cosmic energy from all around you, exhaling any energy blocks. (pause)

Continue to breathe this way for a few breaths.

Inhaling cosmic energy, exhaling any energy blocks. (pause for 3 breaths)

Externalization

Now bring your awareness back to your heart centre. (pause)

Notice the heart centre rising on inhalation, falling on exhalation. (pause)

Bring awareness back to your body.

Yoga Nidra is now complete. (pause)

Feel your body peacefully resting. (pause)

Feel the support beneath you. (pause)

Notice the temperature of the space you're in. (pause)

Notice the sounds. (pause)

Introduce more movement in the body by taking a few deep breaths. (pause)

Now wiggle your fingers and toes. Feel the energy come back to the body like electrical currents.

Stretch or move your body any way you like. Continue to feel the energy coming back to the body. (pause)

And if you're lying down, when you're ready, roll to your right side. Take a few deep breaths here. Recalling any experiences from your practice today. (pause)

If you were lying down, slowly, gently press yourself up to sitting, keep your eyes closed if you can, and take a deep breath. Notice the energy rising as you sit upright. (pause)

We'll finish by chanting Om three times and Shanti three times. Om is a universal vibration. Shanti means peace. Feel the energy continue to rise with the chant.

Om, Om, Om, Shanti, Shanti, Shanti (pause)

When you're ready, softly open your eyes and bring the rested, rejuvenated sensation into the room and into the rest of your day.

Anytime Balanced Thinking *(15 min.)*

A quick practice for balancing the use of your brain hemispheres for more balanced thinking.

Suggested Pre- and Post-Practices:

- Use before or after a yoga class or other healing treatment. Or if using as a standalone practice, consider beginning with a minute or two of simple stretches to release bodily tension – such as seated or standing shoulder rolls, twist, side bend and forward fold.

- Prepare with a few minutes of Hakini Mudra for connection of brain hemispheres and improving intuition.

Settling

Getting comfortable, lying down or sitting, supported.

Choosing any position that's comfortable right now. Getting ready for this practice for more balanced thinking.

Tucking a thin pillow or blanket under your head if you like.

Cover yourself with a blanket if you like.

Doing anything you need to do to get as comfortable as possible. (long pause)

Check for any lumps or bumps of clothing, jewellery, or anything else that might distract you.

If you find any, adjust them now. (pause)

Scan your whole body, making sure you're as comfortable as can be. Feet relaxed… legs… hips… back… arms… shoulders… jaw…

forehead. Checking in and making any further adjustments if it will help you be your most comfortable. (pause)

Feel yourself settling in. (pause)

And now, setting aside anything that's happened before this moment.

Setting aside anything that's happening after this practice.

Bring all of your awareness into your practice for the next 15 minutes.

Setting everything aside for these moments to rebalance and reset. (pause)

Take a deep breath in… and as you exhale, letting go.

Let go of any thoughts, any need to do. Just being.

This is your time for yourself.

No goal, no destination. Just experiencing peace. (pause)

Make any final adjustments if you haven't already. (pause)

Begin to experience the stillness even more. Know that you can move, but if it feels good, allow yourself to enjoy this stillness. This chance to do nothing.

Resting. Just as you like.

If it feels restful, allow these words to be received energetically, rather than mentally. Even the mind can rest now.

In its place, there is effortless awareness. (pause)

Feel all experience becoming more and more effortless.

Serene and effortless. (pause)

Yoga Nidra has now begun. (pause)

Rotation of Consciousness

Now beginning the process of sweeping energy throughout the body.

Making energetic connections from point to point.

Like drawing electrical currents, beams of light, or any other way you experience energetic connection.

Sweep awareness over to the right hand

The right hand thumb

Tip of the index finger

Tip of the middle finger

Tip of the ring finger

Tip of the little finger

Drawing over to the left hand thumb – energetic current, beam of light, or another way of experiencing

Tip of the index finger

Tip of the middle finger

Tip of the ring finger

Tip of the little finger

Over to the right wrist

Then the left wrist

Right elbow

Left elbow

Connecting energy

Right shoulder

Left shoulder

Hollow of the throat

Back of the head near the top

Crown of the head

Eyebrow centre

Right eyebrow

Left eyebrow

Right eye

Left eye

Right ear

Left ear

Right cheek

Left cheek

Tip of the nose

Upper lip

Lower lip

Tip of the chin

Hollow of the throat

Heart centre

Right side of the chest

Heart centre

Left side of the chest

Heart centre

Navel centre

Tip of the tailbone

Right hip

Left hip

Right knee

Left knee

Sweeping energy

Right ankle

Left ankle

Right big toe

Second toe

Third toe

Fourth toe

Little toe

Left big toe

Second toe

Third toe

Fourth toe

Little toe

Now the whole right side of the body

The whole left side of the body

The whole body together

The whole body together

The whole body together (pause)

Welcome the whole body of energetic connections, all at once. (pause)

Breath Awareness

Now become aware of the breath in the nostrils. Just as it is. No need to do anything.

Simply be aware of the breath.

Notice the breath coming in like two streams, through the nostrils. (pause)

Feel the streams flowing in along the floor of the nasal passages.

And feel the breath flowing out.

Streams of air flowing in along the floor of the nasal passages.

And streams of air flowing out. (pause)

Bring awareness to your right nostril.

Follow the inhalation through your right nostril, and as you exhale, feel it flow out through your left.

Keep awareness on the left nostril as you inhale, and exhale feel the breath flow out through the right.

Mental alternate nostril breathing. Inhale through the right.

Exhale through the left.

Inhale through the left.

Exhale through the right.

Inhale through the right, count 1.

Exhale through the left, count 2.

Inhale through the left, count 3.

Exhale through the right, count 4.

Keep counting, up to 26.

If you lose track, start again. (pause for 1 minute)

Now let go of the count. It doesn't matter what number you got to or if the mind wandered. Letting go of the count.

Externalization

Bring your awareness back to your heart centre. (pause)

Notice the heart centre rising on inhalation, falling on exhalation. (pause)

Bring awareness back to your body.

Yoga Nidra is now complete. (pause)

Feel your body peacefully resting. (pause)

Feel the support beneath you. (pause)

Notice the temperature of the space you're in. (pause)

Notice the sounds. (pause)

Introduce more movement in the body by taking a few deep breaths. (pause)

Now wiggle your fingers and toes. Feel the lightness of the sensation.

Stretch or move your body any way you like. (pause)

And if you're lying down, when you're ready, roll to your right side. And take a few deep breaths here. Taking with you any positive feelings from your practice today. (pause)

If you were lying down, slowly, gently press yourself up to sitting, keep your eyes closed if you can, and take a deep breath. (pause)

We'll finish by chanting Om three times and Shanti three times. Om is a universal vibration. Shanti means peace.

Om, Om, Om, Shanti, Shanti, Shanti (pause)

When you're ready, softly open your eyes and bring the balanced sensation into the room and into the rest of your day.

Anytime Sankalpa Renewal *(15 min.)*

Refresh yourself with the inspiring felt-sense of your sankalpa and replant it once again.

Suggested Pre- and Post-Practices:

- This practice assumes some familiarity with the concept of sankalpa. If needed, spend some time explaining the basics. (See page X for detail.)

- Use before or after a yoga class or other healing treatment. Or if using as a standalone practice, consider beginning with a minute or two of simple stretches to release bodily tension – such as seated or standing shoulder rolls, twist, side bend and forward fold.

- Prepare with a few minutes of a heart-centering mudra like Hridaya Mudra or Anjali Mudra.

Settling

Getting comfortable, lying down or sitting, supported.

Choosing any position that's comfortable right now. Getting ready for this practice of refreshing the felt-sense of your sankalpa, or if you don't have a sankalpa, choosing one that feels right in the moment.

Tucking a thin pillow or blanket under your head if you like.

Cover yourself with a blanket if you like.

Doing anything you need to do to get as comfortable as possible. (long pause)

Check for any lumps or bumps of clothing, jewellery, or anything else that might distract you.

If you find any, adjust them now. (pause)

Scan your whole body, making sure you're as comfortable as can be. Feet relaxed… legs… hips… back… arms… shoulders… jaw… forehead. Checking in and making any further adjustments if it will help you be your most comfortable. (pause)

Feel yourself settling in. (pause)

And now, setting aside anything that's happened before this moment.

Setting aside anything that's happening after this practice.

Bring all of your awareness into your practice for the next 15 minutes.

Setting everything else aside for these moments to refresh and reconnect.

Take a deep breath in… and as you exhale, letting go.

Let go of any thoughts, any need to do. Just being.

This is your time for yourself.

Your time to simply enjoy peace. (pause)

Make any final adjustments if you haven't already. (pause)

Begin to experience the stillness even more. Know that you can move, but if it feels good, allow yourself to enjoy this stillness. This chance to do nothing.

Resting. Just as you like.

If it feels restful, allow these words to be received energetically, rather than mentally. Even the mind can rest now.

In its place, there is effortless awareness. (pause)

Feel all experience becoming more and more effortless.

Serene and effortless. (pause)

Yoga Nidra has now begun. (pause)

Sankalpa

Now is the time to state your sankalpa, or heart-felt resolve.

If you already have a sankalpa, allow the joyful feeling of it to arise now. (pause)

If you don't have a sankalpa, you can use: "I am healthy", "I am peaceful", "I am energized" or anything that spontaneously arises in your mind.

Really feel the sankalpa, picture it – as vividly as you can. What does it look like? What does it sound like? How do you feel? (pause)

If the feeling is there, your sankalpa can't help but be manifested.

Right now, state your sankalpa, 3 times with certainty and feeling. (pause)

Your sankalpa has been received and is already being manifested.

Rotation of Consciousness

Now a series of energetic points will be named.

Allow the awareness to float effortlessly from point to point.

Start by floating awareness to the point between the eyebrows

Effortless awareness of the point between the eyebrows

The hollow of the throat

The right shoulder joint

Floating awareness

The right elbow joint

Wrist joint

The right thumb

Tip of the index finger

Tip of the middle finger

Tip of the ring finger

Tip of the little finger

Effortless awareness

The right wrist joint

Elbow joint

Shoulder joint

Hollow of the throat

Shifting awareness over to the left shoulder joint

Elbow joint

Wrist joint

The left thumb

Tip of the index finger

Tip of the middle finger

Tip of the ring finger

Tip of the little finger

Shifting freely

The left wrist joint

Elbow joint

Shoulder joint

Hollow of the throat

The heart centre

The right side of the chest

The heart centre

The left side of the chest

The heart centre

The heart centre

The heart centre

Resting awareness at the heart centre. Not thinking, just feeling. (pause)

Breath Awareness

Notice the chest gently rising and falling with each breath.

Nothing for you to do.

The body is breathing itself.

Simply witnessing. (pause)

Now bring awareness to the nostrils. (pause)

Move awareness to the right nostril.

Feel that with each breath stream coming in the right nostril, action and passion are stimulated.

Right nostril, action and passion stimulated. (pause for 3 breaths)

Now move awareness to the left nostril.

Feel that with each breath stream coming in the left nostril, relaxation and calm are stimulated.

Left nostril, relaxation and calm. (pause for 3 breaths)

Now bring awareness to both nostrils and feel the balance of two streams of breath coming in, right and left, passionate action and relaxing calm.

Take a few deep breaths now, fully awake and aware, feeling a balance of passionate action and relaxing calm. (pause for 3 breaths)

Sankalpa

Now allow your sankalpa to arise again.

Allow your sankalpa to arise again in words and feeling.

Really feel the sankalpa, picture it – as vividly as you can. (pause)

If the feeling is there, it can't help but be manifested.

Right now, state your sankalpa, 3 times with clarity and feeling. (pause)

Your sankalpa has been received and is already being manifested.

Rest now in the joyful feeling of your manifested sankalpa. (pause for 30 seconds)

Externalization

Now bring awareness back to the heart centre.

Notice the heart centre rising on inhalation, falling on exhalation.

Bring awareness back to your body.

Feel your body peacefully resting.

Yoga Nidra is now complete. (pause)

Feel the support beneath you. (pause)

Notice the temperature of the space you're in. (pause)

Notice the sounds. (pause)

Introduce more movement in the body by taking a deep breath. (pause)

Now wiggle your fingers and toes. Feel the energy come back to the body like electrical currents.

Stretch or move your body any way you like. Continue to feel the energy coming back to the body. (pause)

And if you're lying down, when you're ready, roll to your right side. Take a few deep breaths here. Remember your sankalpa and the wonderful feeling of your sankalpa once more. Hold that feeling with you. (pause)

If you were lying down, slowly, gently press yourself up to sitting, keep your eyes closed if you can, and take a deep breath. (pause)

We'll finish by chanting Om three times and Shanti three times. Om is a universal vibration. Shanti means peace.

Om, Om, Om, Shanti, Shanti, Shanti (pause)

When you're ready, softly open your eyes and bring the beautiful feeling of your sankalpa into the room and into the rest of your day.

Overflowing Heart Yoga Nidra *(20 min.)*

Align with the felt-sense of unconditional love and allow it to spill over into everything you do.

Suggested Pre- and Post-Practices:

- A nice one to use at the end of a yoga class for the final savasana or after any type of energy therapy such as reiki, reflexology, massage.

- Prepare or finish with a few minutes of Hridaya Mudra, Abhaya Hridaya Mudra, or Anjali Mudra to connect with the energy of the spiritual heart.

- Prepare or finish with a Shanti Mantra such as:

    Sarvesham svastir bhavatu

    Sarvesham shantir bhavatu

    Sarvesham purnam bhavatu

    Sarvesham mangalam bhavatu

    (May prosperity be unto all, may peace be unto all, may fullness be unto all, may auspiciousness be unto all)

Settling

Getting comfortable, lying down on your back, on your side or sitting, supported.

Getting ready for your Yoga Nidra practice of sleep, with trace awareness.

Getting ready to connect with the heart.

Maybe tucking a thin pillow or blanket under your head.

Covering yourself with a blanket if you like.

Doing anything you need to do to get as comfortable as possible. (long pause for settling)

Let go of anything you think you need to do. (pause)

There is nothing to do right now.

Just shifting from *doing* to *being*. (pause)

Legs are relaxed. (pause)

Feet relaxed. (pause)

Arms relaxed. (pause)

Shoulders are away from the ears. (pause)

Neck is lengthened and relaxed. (pause)

Check for any lumps or bumps of clothing, jewellery, or anything else that might distract you from your Yoga Nidra practice.

If you find any, adjust them now. (pause)

Scan your whole body, making sure you're as comfortable as can be. (pause)

Take a deep breath in… and as you exhale, letting go.

Let go of any thoughts, any need to do. Just being.

This is your time for yourself.

Nothing to accomplish. No to-do list. No striving. Just simply enjoying peace. (pause)

Make any final adjustments if you haven't already.

Begin to feel stillness. Know that you can move, but relish the sweetness of this stillness. This simple being. (pause)

So simple, yet so free. Everything is here for you in this stillness. (pause)

Receiving these words effortlessly.

Effortless awareness.

No need for concentration or thinking.

Let the mind rest. Be aware with your heart. (pause)

Yoga Nidra has now begun. (pause)

Sankalpa

Now is the time to state a heart-felt resolve – a *sankalpa*.

If you already have a sankalpa, allow the joyful feeling of it to arise now.

If you don't have a sankalpa, simply allow an "I am" statement that fills you with joy to arise. For example, "I am calm", "I am healthy", or "I am free". Whatever stirs your heart. No need for thinking, just feeling. Finishing this statement: I am… (pause)

Did anything spontaneously come to mind and fill your heart?

Don't overthink it. Go with that. That is your perfect next step forward.

If nothing came to mind, you can use: "I am calm", "I am healthy", or "I am free".

Really feel your sankalpa, picture it – as vividly as you can. (pause)

If the feeling is there, it can't help but be manifested.

State your sankalpa now, 3 times with clarity and feeling. (pause)

Rotation of Consciousness

Now taking a trip to energy points accessed through the body.

Noticing any sensations, energies or visions that might arise, but remaining free from them. Simply travelling on – carefree.

There's nothing you're looking for, no goal, just being.

Mind is quiet, heart is aware.

Start by bringing awareness to the point between the eyebrows

Effortless awareness of the point between the eyebrows

The hollow of the throat

30

The right shoulder joint

Elbow joint

Wrist joint

The right thumb

The tip of the index finger

Tip of the middle finger

Tip of the ring finger

Tip of the little finger

Effortless awareness

The right wrist joint

Elbow joint

Shoulder joint

Hollow of the throat

Over to the left shoulder joint

Elbow joint

Wrist joint

The left thumb

Tip of the index finger

Tip of the middle finger

Tip of the ring finger

Tip of the little finger

The left wrist joint

Elbow joint

Shoulder joint

Hollow of the throat

The heart centre

The right side of the chest

The heart centre

The left side of the chest

The heart centre

The heart centre

The heart centre

Fix awareness at the heart centre, effortlessly, without thinking, just feeling. (pause)

Breath Awareness

Notice your chest filling with each breath. It's filling with oxygen, to vitalize all of your body. (pause)

And also, energetically, you're pulling in vital life force, known as prana.

This is the key to your vitality.

With each deep breath in, your body receives more of this life force that it needs.

With each deep breath in, your body is fed the energy it needs, and silently, sighs with relief.

Take a deep breath in... and hold until your body naturally wants to let go... then exhale.

No need to force. Find the easy, relaxed rhythm that feels just right.

Inhale filling with oxygen, with energy, holding as the energy is received and dispersed, and exhaling the silent sigh of relief.

Continue breathing this way.

Deep but relaxed inhale... soft holding... and long effortless exhale.

Inhaling energy... retaining gently... and letting go of any effort as you exhale.

Once more.

Inhale... softly hold... effortlessly exhale.

Symbols/Visualization

Now bring awareness back to your heart centre. (pause)

Picture at your heart centre a beautiful glowing light in your favourite colour. (pause)

There is love in this light. (pause)

For a moment, you see a vision of unconditional love in the light.

A person, a pet, a beautiful place, a divine image, that strikes the chord of unconditional love in your heart.

Image of unconditional love at the heart centre, illuminated by the glowing light. (long pause)

Hold awareness of it.

Allow it to fill your heart centre with the *feeling* of unconditional love. (pause)

As the feeling grows, the light glows brighter, pulsing. (pause)

And now, allow the image to dissolve, but hold the feeling of it. Hold the feeling of love.

Feel that the loving light can no longer be contained to the heart centre.

Feel the love light begin to expand out and as it expands, the light is pulsing, radiating.

Feel it expand and *flow*, out beyond your heart centre. Overflowing.

Flowing out, throughout your whole body. Down through the arms to the fingertips. Down through the legs to the toes.

Love light radiating out, even beyond the body.

Spilling over. Creating a field of loving light all around you. (pause)

You are surrounded by loving light.

Bright, warm, comforting, alive. (pause)

Sankalpa

While you're settled here in this deep, peaceful state of love, allow your sankalpa, your heart's desire to arise again.

Allow the feeling of your sankalpa to arise. (pause)

Repeat your sankalpa mentally, with full feeling and awareness, 3 times now. (pause)

Feel that the sankalpa has again been planted, like a seed.

In this deep part of your being, where seed-thoughts begin to grow into beautiful realities.

Feel the beauty of your sankalpa, your heart's desire, growing from deep within you. Blossoming at your heart centre, like a radiant flower. (pause)

Your soul will manifest anything you tell it to.

This how your soul shows its unconditional love for you.

You are always held by your soul's unconditional love for you.

You are always held by your soul's unconditional love for you. (pause)

Feel that love at your heart centre. (pause)

Rest now in that unconditional love, peace, and deep comfort for the next few minutes. (pause for 3 minutes)

Externalization

Ommmmmmmm

If your mind has wandered off, bring your awareness back to your heart centre.

Notice the heart centre swelling as you inhale.

And releasing as you exhale.

Notice your chest, rising on inhalation, falling on exhalation. (pause)

Bring awareness back to your body.

Yoga Nidra is now complete. (pause)

Feel your body resting, still. (pause)

Introduce more movement in the body by taking a few deep breaths. (long pause)

Hold the sensation of your overflowing heart as you bring awareness back to the body. (pause)

Wiggle your fingers and toes. Feel the lightness of the sensation.

Stretch or move your body any way you like. And feel the sensation of love at the heart centre evenly flow out and disperse, to all parts of the body as you stretch. (pause)

And if you're lying down, when you're ready, roll to your right side.

Take a few deep breaths and repeat your sankalpa mentally one more time. (pause)

Feel it fill your heart and overflow to your whole body, radiating out. (pause)

If you were lying down, press yourself up to sitting, eyes closed, chest lifted, and take a deep breath. (pause)

We'll finish by chanting Om three times and Shanti three times. Om is a universal vibration. Shanti means peace.

Om, Om, Om, Shanti, Shanti, Shanti (pause)

When you're ready, open your eyes and bring the awareness of your overflowing heart into the room and into the rest of your day.

Guided Sankalpa Setting *(20 min.)*

Relax the body, allow the thinking mind to settle, and discover your heart's desire arising from deep within you.

Suggested Pre- and Post-Practices:

- This is a great exercise for participants who are new to Yoga Nidra, but it can also be useful for experienced practitioners who might have previously been thinking their way to the sankalpa rather than listening in to the heart's call.

- Begin the session with a preparatory talk about sankalpa. In practice, a sankalpa is a short, positive statement in the present tense that expresses the heart's desire or heart-felt resolve. For example, "I am healthy" or "I am calm". In Yoga Nidra practice, we plant the sankalpa in the subconscious mind and causal, karmic body. It helps us transform ourselves and our lives in intentional ways, manifesting new realities from the inside, out.

- Be sure to remind participants of the importance of not thinking their way to the sankalpa but listening in to what the heart calls for. Prepare them by letting them know that once the heart speaks, the mind might quickly jump in to judge, criticize, analyze and discredit. Let them know that they are free to let go of the shoulds and shouldn'ts. They are free to answer the heart's call if it feels right.

- Begin or finish by holding a heart-centering mudra for a few minutes, such as Abhaya Hridaya Mudra (Fearless Heart).

- Begin or finish with some bhakti yoga, or a peace mantra such as:

  Sarvesham svastir bhavatu

  Sarvesham shantir bhavatu

  Sarvesham purnam bhavatu

  Sarvesham mangalam bhavatu

  (May prosperity be unto all, may peace be unto all, may fullness be unto all, may auspiciousness be unto all)

Getting ready to discover your sankalpa.

Getting ready to lie down on your back, or side, or sit up, supported.

Getting comfortable.

Loosen any tight clothing or jewellery that might distract you. (pause)

Propping yourself with cushions, bolsters, blankets, exactly as you like.

Maybe a soft cushion or blanket under your head.

Maybe a blanket or bolster under your knees.

Covering yourself with a blanket if you like. (long pause for settling)

Checking for any lumps or bumps in the surface beneath you that might distract you. And if you find any, adjust them now. (pause)

Making yourself comfortable for this sankalpa discovery, and once you're comfortable, sinking in. (long pause)

This is an experience taking you deep into the heart to discover your sankalpa, your heart's desire or heart-felt resolve.

A sankalpa is something we use in Yoga Nidra to help us manifest things in our lives.

It's a short statement, in the present tense. Something like: "I am whole", "I am healthy", "I accept myself as I am".

In this experience you're going to *discover* what your heart's desire is.

If you try to "decide" or think your way to your sankalpa, it won't hold as much power.

A sankalpa needs to come from the heart.

Allow the mind to surrender, so the heart can be heard. (pause)

Let go of any ideas about what you *should* want, to allow the message of what you *do* want to naturally arise.

Let go of thinking your way through and shift to feeling. (pause)

Relaxing your body. (pause)

Taking some deep breaths.

Adjusting any body parts you need to, to become completely comfortable.

If you need something else, anything else, to make yourself comfortable, go ahead and give yourself that now. (pause)

Allowing yourself to feel fully supported so you can completely sink in. (pause)

As you start to settle in, notice the stillness that is behind the movement.

The stillness that is there. (pause)

And allow yourself to settle into that stillness.

Deeply letting go to gravity. (pause)

Nothing to think about.

This isn't a thinking practice, it's a feeling practice.

Nothing to think.

Simply feeling. (pause)

Listening with your whole body, allowing the words to be received energetically rather than mentally. (pause)

Now becoming aware of the breath in the nostrils.

Feel the cool air coming in.

And notice the warm air going out.

Notice each breath, cool on the inhalation.

And warm on the exhalation.

Notice also that as you inhale, your abdomen rises, chest rises.

And as you exhale, the abdomen falls and chest falls.

Inhaling abdomen rises and chest expands.

Exhale abdomen falls and chest falls.

Allowing awareness now to start to drop down from the head into the body.

Awareness dropping down from the head, down into the heart centre. (pause)

Bring awareness to the heart centre.

Feel all awareness coming to the heart centre. (pause)

And right now, shift from thinking, to feeling.

Let go of everything you think you know. (pause)

Breathe in and allow a golden, glowing light to arise at the heart centre. (pause)

Breathing in beautiful, glowing light.

Allow the heart space to fill up with that beautiful golden light.

Each breath, more and more of that beautiful glowing light at the heart centre.

Filling the heart centre. (pause)

Heart is so filled with glowing light, it can no longer be contained.

Allow it to spill out, flowing out to all parts of your body. Beautiful glowing light. Flowing out in all directions. To the arms, the legs, and beyond.

So much light. A never-ending stream, flowing out.

Beautiful glowing light, flowing out from the heart centre to all parts of the body and beyond. (long pause)

Now bring awareness back to the heart centre, the epicentre of this flowing light.

Awareness of the light at the heart centre.

Allow the image of a person, a place or an activity you dearly love to arise in that glowing light at the heart centre.

A person, a place or an activity that lights you up. That makes you feel alive.

Don't think too much. Anything that lights you up.

Allow the image to arise in the heart space and then, absorb those positive feelings.

Allow those feelings to fill you with joy.

Feeling it in every pore of your being. (pause)

Absolute joy. (pause)

Now, in that radiant warmth of joy, that loving light, that stream of unlimited potential at the heart centre, ask yourself:

What do I deeply desire?

What is my heart calling me to? (short pause)

What spontaneously arises?

No need to think. Just feel.

If your mind interrupts, just ignore.

Allow the heart to speak freely. (pause)

Imagine yourself being or doing the thing that your heart deeply desires. (pause)

What does it look like? (pause)

How does it sound? (pause)

How are you? (pause)

Don't second-guess.

Try to see it in as much detail as you can. Vividly. (pause)

Now what is the feeling? How do you feel? (pause)

Put it into a few key words in the present tense as your sankalpa.

I am….. or I have…..(pause)

And check again with those few specific words. Are they really lighting you up or is it not quite right yet?

Repeat the words in your mind and notice the feeling. (pause)

Does it fully resonate in that space of absolute joy and light? (pause)

If not, try to make sure it's just right. Adjusting the words in any way you need. And if it is just right, rest in that beautiful feeling. (pause)

If you've gotten lost, go back to that sensation of joy throughout every aspect of your being.

Repeat the sankalpa and check to see that it fully resonates. That the joy remains as full and not dimmed in any way. Perhaps the joy even expands more. (pause)

Now resting in the feeling of your sankalpa for a few moments here. Allow it to sink in, deeply. Permeating every part of your being.

Resting in the beautiful, joyful feeling of your sankalpa now. (pause for 1 minute)

Now bringing your awareness back to your breath.

Noticing the breath in the nostrils, cool on the in-breath, warm on the out-breath. (pause)

Notice the subtle movement in the body as you breathe (pause)

You can make those movements larger now by taking a deep breath. (pause)

Feeling movement breaking up the stillness.

Start to wiggle your fingers and your toes. (pause)

Stretching your body from head to toe when you're ready. (pause)

And if you're lying down, rolling yourself slowly to the right side.

Taking a few breaths here. Once again, recalling the sankalpa if you were able to discover one. If not, try again another time.

Carrying your sankalpa into your day.

You can come back to it any time.

Knowing that your sankalpa will be manifested. Feeling it deeply. (long pause)

If you were lying down, press yourself up to sitting when you're ready, eyes closed.

Taking a deep breath in… and exhale.

Taking another deep breath in and we'll finish with the mantra of Om. Join in if you like.

Om Om Om Shanti Shanti Shanti (pause)

And when you're ready, softly, slowly open your eyes and carry your sankalpa with you as you adjust back into the room and back into your day.

Pure Awareness Yoga Nidra
(25-30 min.)

Discover what lies beyond all doing. Drop into the essence of your own Self. Rest in the peace of your own Self.

Suggested Pre- and Post-Practices:

- Prepare or finish with a few minutes of chanting Om, holding Chin Mudra or any meditative mudra to connect with the nature of the Self.

- Prepare or finish with a wholeness mantra such as:

- Om Purnamadah Purnamidam

  Purnat Purnam Udacyate

  Purnasya Purnamadaya

  Purnamaivavashisyate

  Om Shanti Shanti Shanti

  (That is whole, this is whole. From that whole this whole arises. From that whole, when this whole is negated, what remains is whole.)

- Be sure to leave a good amount of time after this session for practitioners to sit with the experience and transition back into their day. No Yoga Nidra should be rushed, but especially one such as this that connects people to their most subtle reality.

Settling

Getting comfortable – lying on your back or if it's not comfortable, lying on your side, or sitting up, supported.

Getting ready for this Yoga Nidra practice of sleep, with trace awareness.

Maybe making a cozy rest nest with cushions, blankets, bolsters – whatever your body needs to feel as comfortable as possible in this moment. (long pause for settling)

Getting ready to do nothing. (pause)

Nothing you need to do.

Nothing you need to be.

Nothing you need to feel.

No one you need to please.

There is only *you*.

No expectation.

No goal.

No agenda.

No way you can get this wrong.

There's nothing you need to think about.

Just getting comfortable now for this practice of non-doing.

Adjusting your body or your props in any way you need so you can sink into the comfort. (pause)

Check in with how you feel.

Your set-up should make you feel at ease, but not sleepy.

If you do feel sleepy, you could make it slightly less warm, slightly less dark.

You can also check your head position. If your chin is tucked in, it can stimulate sleep. Try moving your head into a neutral alignment, chin neither tucked nor raised, and notice how it might change your energy and alertness. Try moving your head into a position where you feel relaxed yet still alert, not sleepy. (pause)

Set yourself up so you can stay awake and aware, and at the same time, in peaceful ease.

Check that your feet and ankles are relaxed. (pause)

Calves, knees and thighs relaxed. (pause)

Hips relaxed. (pause)

Lower back, middle back, upper back relaxed. Whole back, melting. (pause)

Hands and arms relax. (pause)

Shoulders and neck relax. (pause)

Jaw, tongue and cheeks relax. (pause)

Eyes, forehead and scalp relax. (pause)

Whole body is completely relaxed. (pause)

Nothing to do. (pause)

Body is at ease. (pause)

Awareness continues on. (pause)

Yoga Nidra has now begun. (pause)

Rotation of Consciousness

Bring awareness within the body.

Experiencing energetically rather than physically.

Several points will be mentioned.

They are energetic pathways.

Allow attention to move freely from one point to the next. No need to concentrate, just moving awareness. Effortlessly.

If at any time you feel the urge to let go of the guidance and drop into meditation, then drop in.

If at any time you need to move, then move.

Be effortless.

Begin with awareness of the energetic point between the eyebrows.

Effortless awareness of the point between the eyebrows.

The hollow of the throat

Shifting freely, unattached

The right shoulder joint

Elbow joint

Wrist joint

The right thumb

The tip of the index finger

Tip of the middle finger

Tip of the ring finger

Tip of the little finger

Experiencing energetically

The right wrist joint

Elbow joint

Shoulder joint

Hollow of the throat

Over to the left shoulder joint

Elbow joint

Wrist joint

The left thumb

Tip of the index finger

Tip of the middle finger

Tip of the ring finger

Tip of the little finger

Back up to the left wrist joint

Elbow joint

Shoulder joint

Hollow of the throat

The heart centre

The right side of the chest

The heart centre

The left side of the chest

The heart centre

The navel centre

Tip of the tailbone

The right hip joint

Right knee joint

Ankle joint

The right big toe

Tip of the second toe

Tip of the third toe

Tip of the fourth toe

Tip of the baby toe

Back up to the right ankle joint

Knee joint

Hip joint

Tip of the tailbone

Sweeping awareness to the left hip joint

Left knee joint

Ankle joint

The left big toe

Tip of the second toe

Tip of the third toe

Tip of the fourth toe

Tip of the baby toe

Back up to the left ankle joint

Knee joint

Hip joint

Tip of the tailbone

The navel centre

The heart centre

Hollow of the throat

The eyebrow centre

The eyebrow centre

The eyebrow centre (pause)

Breath Awareness

Feel as if you are breathing in and out through the point between the eyebrows. (pause)

In a straight line, from the point between the eyebrows to the centre of the brain. (pause)

Breathing like this for several breaths now. (pause for 4-5 breaths)

Allow the breath to become subtle. (pause)

Breathing in a straight line, from the point between the eyebrows to the centre of the brain. (pause)

Breath becoming subtler and subtler. (pause)

Until the breath is almost imperceptible. (long pause)

Symbols/Visualization

(Read slowly)

Almost all doing has halted.

Only listening remains.

Preparing to leave even the listening behind, to experience what lies beyond.

When all doing ends, what remains is pure awareness.

Ever free, ever present.

Present through doing and non-doing.

Constant. Eternal.

Awareness is what remains when all doing ends.

Pure awareness. (pause)

This is your essence.

THIS is who you are.

You, the awareness, are present through of all of your waking life, dreaming life, deep sleep and once again when you wake.

You are the thread.

You are the awareness.

Aware through the pleasant and unpleasant, success and failure. Yet, ever *free and unaffected* by any.

Free and unaffected.

You are the pure awareness.

There beneath all the thinking and doing, you are at peace.

You *are* peace.

You are the peace you've been looking for all along. You, yourSelf. (pause)

There is nothing to seek.

Nothing to gain.

No distance between what you seek and what you already are.

You are it.

So now, allow the brain to rest.

There is nothing left to do.

Release the mind. Like an instrument you're holding onto.

Release the mind.

Let it go.

Drop into the stillness and silence that remains.

Drop into the stillness and silence.

Rest in the peace of your own Self. (pause for 4-10 min.)

Externalization

Ommmmmm

Bringing awareness back to the breath. Notice your body breathing. Feel your body breathing.

Take a moment to enjoy the non-doing of your breathing. (long pause)

Now take a deep breath.

Feel energy and awareness coming back into the body.

Yoga Nidra is now complete. (pause)

Take another breath. (pause)

And if you feel like making gentle movements in the body, make them. If you feel like making larger movements, make them. (pause)

Listening in and moving when and how you'd like. (pause)

And if you're lying down, roll to the side if it feels right.

And if you like, take a moment to recall your experience. (pause)

What will you take with you from your experience today? (pause)

Make your way to sitting upright.

Keep the eyes closed if you can.

Feel the energy rising upward as you sit.

Feel the body activating.

The mind activating.

And yet, still remaining relaxed.

I'll finish by chanting Om and Shanti three times each. Join in if you like.

Notice the energy rise with the chant.

Om Om Om Shanti Shanti Shanti (pause)

Slowly, softly open your eyes when you're ready, adjusting back into the room and back into your day, reconnected with the essence of your being.

Energizing Yoga Nidra (25-30 min)

Revive yourself in times of low energy with this prana-cultivating Yoga Nidra practice. Perfect for the winter season or for people working/living mostly indoors or with poor ventilation.

Suggested Pre- and Post-Practices:

- Ideal for the final savasana of a Prana Restorative Yoga class. (See my Prana Restorative Yoga course at tamaraskyhawk.com for details.)

- Begin with some gentle yoga asanas or movements. Be careful not to tire participants out, as they might already have low energy.

- Prepare or finish with a few minutes of Prana Mudra for vitality.

- Prepare or finish with a prana-giving mantra such as:

  Om Haum Joom Saha

- Finish with a few simple stretches or movements like shoulder rolls, seated side bend and twist, as well as a self-massage of the shoulders, neck and scalp to re-energize the physical body.

Settling

Lying down comfortably, or sitting up, supported. Getting ready for this energy-reviving Yoga Nidra practice.

If you're lying down, place a thin pillow or blanket under your head for support, but not so bulky that your head is out of alignment.

Cover yourself with a blanket if you like.

Doing anything you need to do to get comfortable. (long pause)

If you're lying in savasana, legs are apart. Feet flopped out to the sides. Your arms are away from the body, leaving space beneath the armpits. Palms are facing up.

In any position, shoulders are away from the ears. (pause)

Check that your head is comfortable, straight and in alignment. (pause)

Check that everything is just right. (pause)

Let your whole body be as comfortable as can be.

Feel the support of the surface beneath you. Let it hold you as you completely surrender to gravity. (pause)

Letting go into the support. (pause)

Take a deep breath in… and as you exhale, let go of anything you think you need to do right now. There is nothing you need to do. Nothing you have to think about. Set everything aside. (pause)

Bring all of your attention inward. (pause)

Inhale feeling present in this moment.

Exhale letting go of anything outside of this moment.

Inhale feeling present in this moment.

Exhale letting go of anything outside of right here, right now.

Become aware of your body. Be aware of your whole body from the top of your head to the tips of your toes and from the tips of your toes to the crown of your head.

Feel stillness in your whole body.

You can move your body any time you need, but make yourself so comfortable you won't have any desire to move. (pause)

Settle into the comfort.

Absolute comfort.

Stillness.

Effortlessness. (pause)

Awake and aware.

Yoga Nidra has now begun. (pause)

Sankalpa

Now is the time to state your sankalpa, or heart-felt resolve.

If you already have a sankalpa, allow the joyful feeling of it to arise now.

If you don't have a sankalpa, you can use: "I am energized and full of life".

"I am energized and full of life". (pause)

Really feel the sankalpa, picture it – as vividly as you can. (pause)

If the feeling is there, it can't help but be manifested. (pause)

Right now, state your sankalpa, or "I am energized and full of life", 3 times with certainty and feeling. (pause)

Rotation of Consciousness

Now bring your awareness deep inside the body.

An energetic journey is about to begin.

Several body parts will be named.

Sweep awareness swiftly and effortlessly from one to the next.

Experiencing energetically, rather than physically.

Start by bringing awareness to the point between the eyebrows

Effortless awareness of the point between the eyebrows

The hollow of the throat

The right shoulder joint

Elbow joint

Wrist joint

The right thumb

The tip of the index finger

Tip of the middle finger

Tip of the ring finger

Tip of the little finger

Experiencing energetically

The right wrist joint

Elbow joint

Shoulder joint

Hollow of the throat

Over to the left shoulder joint

Elbow joint

Wrist joint

The left thumb

Tip of the index finger

Tip of the middle finger

Tip of the ring finger

Tip of the little finger

Back up to the left wrist joint

Elbow joint

Shoulder joint

Hollow of the throat

The heart centre

The right side of the chest

The heart centre

The left side of the chest

The heart centre

The navel centre

Tip of the tailbone

The right hip joint

Right knee joint

Ankle joint

The right big toe

Tip of the second toe

Tip of the third toe

Tip of the fourth toe

Tip of the baby toe

Back up to the right ankle joint

Knee joint

Hip joint

Tip of the tailbone

Sweeping awareness to the left hip joint

Left knee joint

Ankle joint

The left big toe

Tip of the second toe

Tip of the third toe

Tip of the fourth toe

Tip of the baby toe

Back up to the left ankle joint

Knee joint

Hip joint

Tip of the tailbone

The navel centre

The heart centre

Hollow of the throat

The eyebrow centre

The eyebrow centre

The eyebrow centre (pause)

Breath Awareness

Now become aware of the breath.

No need to change the breath in any way, simply bring awareness to the breath. (pause)

As you exhale, feel that you let go of any fatigue, stress, tension.

As you inhale, feel that you're pulling in *boundless energy*.

Exhale letting go of any fatigue, stress, tension.

Inhale filling up with *boundless energy*.

Exhaling letting go.

Inhaling energizing.

Exhale from the crown of the head down to the toes.

Inhale from the toes up to the crown of the head.

Exhale from the crown of the head down to the ankles.

Inhale from the ankles up to the crown of the head.

Exhale from the crown of the head down to the knees.

Inhale from the knees up to the crown of the head.

Exhale from the crown down the spine to the tailbone.

Inhale from the tailbone up the spine to the crown.

Exhale from the crown down the spine to the navel.

Inhale from the navel up the spine to the crown.

Exhale from the crown down the spine to the heart centre.

Inhale from the heart centre up the spine to the crown.

Exhale from the crown down to the throat centre.

Inhale from the throat centre up the spine to the crown.

Exhale from the crown down to the bridge between the nostrils.

Inhale from the bridge between the nostrils up to the crown.

Now to the third eye, exhale down to the bridge between the nostrils.

Inhale from the bridge between the nostrils, up to the third eye.

Back to the crown, exhale down to the bridge between the nostrils.

Inhale from the bridge between the nostrils up to the crown.

Exhale from the crown down the spine to the throat centre.

Inhale from the throat centre up the spine to the crown.

Exhale from the crown down the spine to the heart centre.

Inhale from the heart centre up the spine to the crown.

Exhale from the crown down the spine to the navel.

Inhale from the navel up the spine to the crown.

Exhale from the crown down the spine to the tailbone.

Inhale from the tailbone up the spine to the crown.

Exhale from the crown of the head down to the knees.

Inhale from the knees up to the crown of the head.

Exhale from the crown of the head down to the ankles.

Inhale from the ankles up to the crown of the head.

Exhale from the crown of head down to the toes.

Inhale from the toes up to the crown of the head. (pause)

Feel that the whole body is breathing in and out. (pause)

Inhaling cosmic energy from all around you, exhaling any energy blocks.

Inhaling cosmic energy from all around you, exhaling any energy blocks. (long pause)

Be aware of the space between the eyebrows.

Feel as if you're breathing in and out from the space between the eyebrows. (long pause)

Be aware of the throat.

Picture a shining full moon.

Bathe in that sublime moonlight.

Allow its rays to calm, clarify and soothe you, *completely*. (pause)

Be aware of the space at the heart centre.

Dive deep within that space.

Deep into the silence.

Awake and aware.

Deep into the stillness and silence at the heart centre. (long pause)

Sankalpa

Now allow your sankalpa to arise again.

Allow your sankalpa to arise in words and feeling.

You might have used your own sankalpa or "I am energized and full of life".

Really feel the sankalpa, picture it – as vividly as you can. (pause)

If the feeling is there, it can't help but be manifested. (pause)

Right now, state your sankalpa, or "I am energized and full of life", 3 times with clarity and feeling. (pause)

Your sankalpa has been received and is already being manifested.

Rest now in the joyful feeling of your manifested sankalpa for the next several minutes. (pause for 3-8 minutes)

Externalization

Ommmmmmmm

Be aware of the space at the heart centre.

Be aware of the deep stillness and silence at the heart centre. (pause)

Be aware that the body is breathing, resting.

Sense the gentle movement of the body at rest, breathing. (pause)

Awaken the stored energy in the body by taking a deep breath in and a long breath out. (pause)

Yoga Nidra is now complete. (pause)

Wiggle your fingers and toes. Feel the energy like electrical sparks in the body. (pause)

Stretch or move your body in any way you like. Feel energy begin to flow through each body part as you move. (pause)

And if you're lying down, when you're ready, roll to your right side.

Take a few deep breaths and mentally repeat your sankalpa or "I am energized and full of life." one more time. Feel it fill your whole being. (pause)

If you were lying down, press yourself up to sitting. Keep your eyes closed if you can.

Take as much time as you need. (long pause)

Sitting up, back as straight as you can make it, top of the head rising toward the ceiling.

Take a few deep breaths in, feeling the energy rising. (pause)

And finally, when you're ready, softly, slowly open your eyes.

Adjusting back into the room, back into your day, refreshed, full of life and in peace.

With eyes softly focused, take a few breaths, taking in this space around you, with awareness of yourself in it. (pause)

Close your eyes once again and we'll finish by chanting Om and Shanti three times each. Om is a universal vibration. Shanti means peace.

Feel the energy rise within you as you chant.

Om Om Om Shanti Shanti Shanti (pause)

Slowly open your eyes again and carry this peacefully energized sensation with you.

Rainbow Light Yoga Nidra *(30 min.)*

Journey to a sacred, luminous rainbow and bathe in its light.

Suggested Pre- and Post-Practices:

- This practice assumes familiarity with the concept of sankalpa. Begin with a brief explanation of sankalpa or the Guided Sankalpa Setting (page X) if you're leading people unfamiliar with sankalpa.

- Begin or finish with Anjali Mudra to inspire feelings of humility and connection.

- Prepare or finish with a Shanti Mantra such as:

    Sarvesham svastir bhavatu

    Sarvesham shantir bhavatu

    Sarvesham purnam bhavatu

    Sarvesham mangalam bhavatu

(May prosperity be unto all, may peace be unto all, may fullness be unto all, may auspiciousness be unto all)

Settling

Getting ready for your Yoga Nidra practice.

This is your time to rest, connect, discover, or take whatever you'd like from this practice today.

Building yourself a comfortable *rest nest*, whatever that might look like.

Lying on your back in savasana, or maybe lying on your side, or sitting up, supported.

Whatever is best for today, give yourself full permission to do that.

Maybe you have a pillow under your head, a blanket covering you, fuzzy socks – whatever is going to help you feel as comfortable as possible. (pause)

Getting as comfortable as possible so you can feel fully supported and free to release tension.

If you like, cover your eyes with a light eye pillow or scarf.

If you feel any tension in your back while you're lying down, place a pillow, rolled blanket or bolster under your knees.

Do all the things you need to do to make yourself sublimely comfortable.

Make any adjustments you need. (long pause)

Make any final adjustments now to feel perfectly at ease. (pause)

Feel your body sinking into the support beneath you.

Body fully supported, effortlessly dropping into a state of peace.

Dropping into a state of non-doing. (pause)

Nothing to do.

Letting go of doing.

Shifting, into being.

Feel your body let go of tensions as you give it this sweet permission to do nothing. (pause)

Feel your body sigh ahhhhhh at this opportunity to do nothing. (pause)

Letting go of doing.

Shifting into being. (pause)

This is the opportunity your body has been waiting for.

The opportunity to relax and renew, in a state of complete *ease*.

Notice the sensation of your body letting go of tension in the shoulders. (pause)

Letting go of tension in the back. (pause)

Letting go of tension in the arms. (pause)

The legs. (pause)

The face. (pause)

Body completely letting go of tension. (pause)

Body is stilling and at ease.

Effortless awareness of this peaceful state of non-doing. (pause)

Allow your awareness to shift now to the sound of the breath. (pause)

Listen closely to this soft sound of the body breathing itself. (pause)

Feel the stillness of the body. The body can move anytime you need, but if you don't need, dive into the peace of the stillness. (pause)

The body rests, while the awareness moves and explores.

Awake.

Aware.

Effortless. (pause)

Yoga Nidra has now begun. (pause)

Sankalpa

Now if you'd like to make a sankalpa, a heart-felt resolve, allow it to arise in your awareness.

Allow the feeling of your sankalpa to arise. (pause)

Vividly see your sankalpa manifested. (pause)

Energetically *feel* your sankalpa manifested. (pause)

And now, repeat your sankalpa mentally, three times with absolute certainty and feeling. (pause)

Feel with certainty that your sankalpa has been received. There's nothing you need to do. Your sankalpa is already being manifested.

Rotation of Consciousness

Now moving awareness within the body.

Experiencing energetically rather than physically.

Several locations will be mentioned.

They are energetic pathways.

Allow attention to move freely from one point to the next. No need to concentrate, just moving awareness.

If sensations or experiences arise, simply take notice and move on.

Begin with effortless awareness of the point between the eyebrows

Effortless awareness of the point between the eyebrows

The hollow of the throat

Shifting freely

The right shoulder joint

Elbow joint

Wrist joint

The right thumb

The tip of the index finger

Tip of the middle finger

Tip of the ring finger

Tip of the little finger

Experiencing energetically

The right wrist joint

Elbow joint

Shoulder joint

Hollow of the throat

Over to the left shoulder joint

Elbow joint

Wrist joint

The left thumb

Tip of the index finger

Tip of the middle finger

Tip of the ring finger

Tip of the little finger

Back up to the left wrist joint

Elbow joint

Shoulder joint

Hollow of the throat

The heart centre

The right side of the chest

The heart centre

The left side of the chest

The heart centre

The navel centre

Tip of the tailbone

The right hip joint

Right knee joint

Ankle joint

The right big toe

Tip of the second toe

Tip of the third toe

Tip of the fourth toe

Tip of the baby toe

Back up to the right ankle joint

Knee joint

Hip joint

Tip of the tailbone

Sweeping awareness to the left hip joint

Left knee joint

Ankle joint

The left big toe

Tip of the second toe

Tip of the third toe

Tip of the fourth toe

Tip of the baby toe

Back up to the left ankle joint

Knee joint

Hip joint

Tip of the tailbone

The navel centre

The heart centre

Hollow of the throat

The eyebrow centre (pause)

Experiencing the whole right side from the crown of the head to the tips of the toes and from the tips of the toes up to the crown of the head.

Now the whole left side from the crown of the head to the tips of the toes and from the tips of the toes up to the crown of the head.

And now the whole body together

The whole body together

The whole body together

Field of energetic sensation

Field of being (pause)

Breath Awareness

Notice this field of being, or the whole body, breathing.

The whole self, breathing. (long pause)

Inhaling, pulling in cosmic energy.

Exhaling, releasing tension.

Inhaling energy.

Exhaling fatigue.

And if it feels good, breathing in light – radiant and energizing.

Exhaling anything you need to release, like dark smoke leaving your being.

Inhaling radiant light.

Exhaling anything you'd like to release, as dark smoke that immediately dissolves.

We'll take a minute now to breathe. Just breathe.

If you like, continue breathing in light, exhaling dark smoke, or return to breathing normally. (pause for 30 seconds)

Symbols/Visualization

And now, visualize yourself resting on a warm, and completely private sandy beach. (pause)

Waves are lapping against the shore, creating a serene setting for rest and reflection. (pause)

You are about to take a sacred pilgrimage to a healing waterfall. (pause)

See your energetic body rise up from your physical body. Energetic body separating from the physical body, ready to explore on this sacred pilgrimage.

You are completely free in your energy body. You can move in any way you like. (pause)

As you fly into the clear blue sky, you see your physical body resting safely and peacefully below you, on this beautiful private beach.

Fly over the lush green jungle. Notice the palm trees, colourful birds, abundant tropical fruits. (pause)

In the distance you see a flowing river.

You fly to the river, following it along as it winds through a rocky range. (pause)

You fly close to the water of the gently flowing river – it is crystal clear and you can see an abundance of plant life growing beneath the water, shiny fish with bold stripes playing amongst the reeds, and smooth stones in many shades. (pause)

You notice the sound of the river is getting much louder.

You look up to see that the river drops off, over a cliff up ahead.

You fly over the cliff and look behind you.

You have arrived here at the sacred waterfall.

It is breathtaking. Crystal clear water falling over grey stone, creating a massive and vibrant rainbow. (pause)

You fly to the base of the rainbow where there is a smooth stone to stand on and only the faintest spray of water – just enough to stay comfortable in this tropical environment. (pause)

You are now standing in this vibrant, luminous rainbow. (pause)

All colours are projected on you. You are bathing in radiant light in every colour. (pause)

Radiant energy. (pause)

One colour is attracting your attention most. (pause)

You notice this and sense that this colour has a healing gift for you. (pause)

You might not know what that gift is, but in this moment, you know you don't *need* to think about it. You can simply enjoy the light and the radiance of this rainbow as your being absorbs whatever it needs. (pause)

Your being knows just what to do. Your being knows exactly why it needs that colour's energy right now.

You stand strong in the radiance of this rainbow for several moments, serene and blissful. Taking in anything you need from this colourful light, without thinking, just feeling. (long pause)

Sankalpa

In this luminous rainbow, allow your sankalpa to arise in your awareness.

Allow the feeling of your sankalpa to arise. (pause)

Repeat your sankalpa three times, with feeling and certainty. (pause)

Know that all you need is here, within you.

Your sankalpa is already being manifested.

You give gratitude for your experience in this rainbow light and prepare to fly back to the private beach. (pause)

You take off from the smooth grey rock, fly up to the top of the cliff and follow the clear, flowing river back. (pause)

Over the jungle you see the vibrant green trees again, the fruits, the birds.

Arriving back over the beach, you see your body resting serenely. (pause)

You come back into the physical body.

Back in the physical body, integrating the experience of your energy body with your physical body. (peace)

Externalization

Bring awareness to your heart centre.

Notice the chest rising and falling with each breath. (pause)

Listen for the sound of the breath. (pause)

Yoga Nidra is now complete. (pause)

Taking a few deep breaths now and notice sensation coming back to the body. (pause)

Wiggle your fingers and toes and feel the energy back in the body like electrical currents.

Stretch or move your body any way you like. And feel energy begin to flow through each body part as you move. (pause)

And if you're lying down, when you're ready, roll to your right side.

Take a few deep breaths and mentally repeat your sankalpa one more time. (pause) Feel it fill your whole being. (pause)

Remember your experience in the rainbow light. What would you like to take with you from your experience today? (pause)

If you were lying down, press yourself up to sitting.

Keep your eyes closed if you can.

Take as much time as you need. (pause)

Sitting up, back as straight as you can make it, top of the head rising toward the ceiling.

Take a few deep breaths in, feeling the energy rising. (pause for 3 breaths)

And finally, when you're ready, softly, slowly open your eyes.

Adjusting awareness back into the room, back into your day, refreshed and in peace.

With eyes softly focused, take a few breaths, taking in this space around you, with awareness of yourself in it. (pause)

Close your eyes once again and we'll finish by chanting Om and Shanti three times each.

Feel the energy rise within you as you chant.

Om Om Om Shanti Shanti Shanti (pause)

And softly open your eyes again, taking any positive experience from your practice today into the room and into the rest of your day.

Releasing Yoga Nidra *(30 min.)*

What are you holding that is holding you back? Check in and release whatever is no longer serving you so you can move forward in freedom.

Suggested Pre- and Post-Practices:

- Begin with a gentle movement sequence to release stiffness from the joints.

- Begin or finish by holding Abhaya Mudra for fearlessness and openness.

Settling

Getting comfortable for this practice of Yoga Nidra, sleep with trace awareness.

Getting ready for an experience of release and the resulting freedom.

Lying on your back or if it's not comfortable, lying on your side, or sitting up, supported.

Maybe making a cozy rest nest with cushions, blankets, bolsters, eye pillow – whatever your body needs to feel as comfortable as possible in this moment. (long pause for settling)

Let go of anything you think you need to do.

There is nothing to do right now.

With ease, shift from *doing* to *being*. (pause)

This time is just for you.

This practice is just for you.

There are no shoulds or shouldn'ts.

There's no way you can do this wrong.

So make yourself as comfortable as you like, in just the way you like.

Adjusting anything you like. Any way you like.

Listening in to what you need. And then answering that request.

You might prefer a lot of cushions, blankets and props, you might prefer just a few, you might even prefer none. All are equally welcome.

Do whatever you need feel supported, held, and free to let go of tensions.

Getting comfortable for this practice of non-doing. (pause)

Check for any lumps or bumps of clothing, jewellery, or anything else that might distract you.

If you find any, adjust them now. (pause)

Take a deep breath in… and as you exhale, release any tension.

Beginning a check now that each body part is as relaxed as can be. If you can't completely relax, that's fine. You're welcome just as you are.

Check that your feet and ankles are relaxed as can be. (pause)

Calves, knees and thighs relaxed as can be. (pause)

Hips relaxed as can be. (pause)

Lower back, middle back, upper back, releasing tension. Whole back, melting. (pause)

Hands and arms letting go. (pause)

Shoulders and neck melting, tension diffusing. (pause)

Jaw, tongue and cheeks softening. (pause)

Eyes, forehead and scalp softening. (pause)

Whole body melting into the support of the earth beneath you. Held by the support of the earth beneath you. (pause)

Take a deep breath in… and as you exhale, release any remaining tension.

Letting go of any thoughts, any need to do. Just being.

This is your time for yourself.

No agenda. Just peace. (pause)

Make any final adjustments if you haven't already.

Begin to feel stillness. Know that you can move anytime you like, but relish the sweetness of this stillness. This simple being.

So simple, yet so free. Everything is here for you in this stillness. (pause)

Receiving these words effortlessly.

No need to do *anything*.

Effortless awareness. (pause)

Yoga Nidra has now begun. (pause)

Rotation of Consciousness

Now taking your effortless awareness around the body from point to point.

Freely shifting awareness, staying unattached.

There's nothing you need to accomplish or experience.

There's no way to get this wrong.

Simply sweeping awareness, free and unattached.

Starting by becoming aware of the right side of the body

Become aware of the right hand

Right hand thumb

Index finger

Middle finger

Ring finger

Little finger

Palm of the hand

Back of the hand

Effortless

Right wrist

Lower arm

Elbow

Upper arm

Shoulder

Armpit

Right side of the ribs

Right side of the waist

Right hip

Thigh

Knee

Lower leg

Ankle

Heel

Sole of the foot

Top of the foot

Right big toe

Second toe

Third toe

Fourth toe

Fifth toe

Awake and aware

Move awareness to the left side of the body

Become aware of the left hand

Left hand thumb

Index finger

Middle finger

Ring finger

Little finger

Palm of the hand

Back of the hand

Left wrist

Lower arm

Elbow

Upper arm

Shoulder

Armpit

Left side of the ribs

Left side of the waist

Left hip

Thigh

Knee

Lower leg

Ankle

Heel

Sole of the foot

Top of the foot

Left big toe

Second toe

Third toe

Fourth toe

Fifth toe

Awake and aware

Shift awareness to the crown of the head

Crown of the head

Forehead

Right temple

Left temple

Right eyebrow

Left eyebrow

Eyebrow centre

Sweeping awareness

Right eye

Left eye

Right ear

Left ear

Right cheek

Left cheek

Right nostril

Left nostril

Upper lip

Lower lip

Chin

Throat centre

Right collarbone

Left collarbone

Right side of the chest

Left side of the chest

Heart centre

Navel

Pelvis

Move awareness to the back of the body

Right buttock

Left buttock

Lower back

Middle back

Upper back

Right shoulder blade

Left shoulder blade

Back of the neck

Back of the head

Crown of the head

Move awareness down to the whole right leg

The whole left leg

Both legs together

The whole torso

The whole right arm

The whole left arm

Neck

Head

The whole front of the body

The whole back of the body

Become aware of the whole body together

The whole body together

The whole body together (long pause)

Breath Awareness/Visualization

Notice this field of being, or the whole body, breathing.

The whole self, breathing. (pause)

Inhaling the peace of simply being.

Exhaling, releasing all tension.

Inhaling the peace of simply being.

And exhaling, releasing, all stress, all tension.

One more time, inhaling the peace of simply being.

And exhaling, releasing, all stress, all tension.

Now inhaling cosmic energy from all around you.

And exhaling, releasing, any fatigue, in body, mind or soul.

Inhaling vibrant energy.

And exhaling, releasing any fatigue.

One more time, inhaling vibrant energy.

And exhaling, releasing any remaining fatigue.

Now inhaling positivity.

Exhaling, releasing any negativity.

Inhaling joyful positivity.

And exhaling, releasing any negativity.

One more time, inhaling positivity, full of joy.

And exhaling, releasing all remaining negativity.

And if it feels good now, breathing in light – radiant and energizing.

And as you exhale, let go of anything you need to release, like dark smoke leaving your being.

Inhaling radiant, energizing light.

Exhaling dark smoke that immediately dissolves.

Inhaling radiant, energizing light, filling your being.

And exhaling anything you'd like to release, as a dark smoke that immediately dissolves.

Continue breathing in this way – taking in positive, radiant light and energy, and exhaling anything you'd like to release, anything holding you back, anything that no longer serves you.

Feel the lightness increasing the more you release.

The openness increasing, personal potential increasing.

Freedom increasing with each exhale of release.

Each release bringing you more freedom, peace and joy.

Continue breathing in this way for several breaths. Inhaling radiant energy, exhaling anything you'd like to release, like dark smoke that immediately dissolves. (pause for 1 minute)

And now, letting go of the visualized breath.

Letting go and returning to breathing normally.

Normal breath.

Effortless breath.

Body breathing itself, peacefully.

There is nothing for you to do.

Simply rest.

Rest in the joyful sensation of lightness, peace, *freedom* for the next few minutes.

(pause for 3 minutes)

Externalization

Become aware of the natural breath again.

Awareness of the natural breath.

Observe the chest rising and falling with each inhalation and exhalation. (pause)

Notice the gentle contraction of the nostrils on inhalation, expansion on exhalation. (pause)

Bring awareness back into the experience of the physical body.

Know that the practice of Yoga Nidra is coming to an end.

Externalize the mind.

Be aware that your body is resting, practicing Yoga Nidra.

Be aware that you are resting in a room.

While keeping your eyes closed, mentally visualize the room you're in.

See the walls. The floor. The objects in the room. Their placement, colour, textures.

Externalize your awareness.

Become aware of the sensations of the physical body – the feel of the body on the surface beneath you. (pause)

The feel of the fabric on your skin. (pause)

The temperature of the air touching your skin. (pause)

Externalize your awareness. (pause)

Yoga Nidra is now complete. (pause)

Beginning movement again in the body, wiggle your fingers, wiggle your toes.

Make any gentle movements with the body that feel good. (pause)

Now make any larger movements – move your feet, legs, hands, arms, move any body parts that are calling you, and if you're lying down, when you're ready, roll to the right side.

Take a few deep breaths, integrating your Yoga Nidra experience into your everyday experience. (pause)

Recalling any sensation of release. Any sensation of increased lightness, peace, joy, potential. (pause)

And if you were lying down, when you're ready, with eyes closed if it feels good, press yourself slowly up to sitting. (pause)

Taking your time, there's no rush.

Sitting comfortably, back as straight as you can make it.

Take a deep breath in… and a long breath out.

Maybe noticing the energy rising as you're now sitting upright.

We'll finish by chanting Om and Shanti, three times each.

Om Om Om Shanti Shanti Shanti (pause)

And slowly, softly open your eyes when you're ready.

Welcome back, with maybe a little more freedom or ease than you had before.

Grounding Yoga Nidra – Shift from Rajas to Sattva *(30 min.)*

Bring awareness down from an over-active mind back into the body, balance your energies, and connect with the grounding element of earth and structure.

Suggested Pre- and Post-Practices:

- This is a great practice for anyone who's feeling overworked, overburdened, stressed or on the rollercoaster of busyness/exhaustion.

- Begin with a yoga asana practice rooted in the lower chakras. For example, a seated sequence of neck stretches, shoulder rolls, forward bends, twists and side bends. Makarasana (crocodile pose) is also very grounding, including the restorative yoga version of Makarasana.

- Prepare or finish with a few minutes of Bhu Mudra or Prithvi Mudra for connection to the elemental energy of earth.

- Prepare or finish with a Shanti Mantra such as:

  Sarvesham svastir bhavatu

  Sarvesham shantir bhavatu

  Sarvesham purnam bhavatu

  Sarvesham mangalam bhavatu

  (May prosperity be unto all, may peace be unto all, may fullness be unto all, may auspiciousness be unto all)

Settling

Lying down comfortably – on your back, your side or your abdomen. Or sitting up, supported.

Any position is fine. Stretched, curled, it doesn't matter.

Listening to the body and choosing the position that best suits you, right now, for this practice of grounding. (pause)

Getting ready for this grounding practice of Yoga Nidra.

Cushioning your head with a pillow or blanket.

Cover yourself with a blanket if it helps you feel grounded. Or maybe two blankets. (pause)

Maybe you'd like to *hug* a bolster or blanket. (pause)

Maybe if you're lying on your abdomen, you'd like the weight of a folded blanket on your back. (pause)

Maybe an eye pillow to soothe your eyes. (pause)

Just listening in and answering the call.

What is your body asking for in this moment? (pause)

Propping and positioning yourself in any way you'd like right now. (long pause)

During this practice, you can move your body any time you need, but make yourself so comfortable you won't want to move. (pause)

Check that everything is just right. (pause)

Check that your feet are comfortable. (pause)

Legs are comfortable. (pause)

Hips are comfortable. (pause)

The whole back. (pause)

Arms and hands. (pause)

Shoulders. (pause)

Neck. (pause)

Jaw, tongue, forehead. (pause)

The whole body, as comfortable as can be. (pause)

Feel the support of the surface beneath you. Let it hold you as you completely surrender to gravity. (pause)

Letting go into the support.

Allow your body to sink into the earth beneath you.

Settling into the earth. (pause)

Held by the earth. Unconditionally. Without expectation. (pause)

Nothing expected of you. Nothing to do. (pause)

Take a deep breath in… and as you exhale, let go of anything you think you need to do right now. (pause)

There's nothing you need to do. Nothing you have to think about. Set everything aside. (pause)

Body is settling in. (pause)

Attention is drawing inward. (pause)

Inhale feeling present in this moment.

Exhale letting go of anything outside of this moment.

Inhale feeling present in this moment.

Exhale letting go of anything outside of right here, right now. (pause)

Allow your sense of hearing to extend out, like a microphone, receiving sounds, but without analyzing. Simply receiving objectively. Receiving any sounds. (pause)

The farthest sounds (pause)

Near sounds (pause)

Maybe even the sounds within your own body. The sound of your own breath. (pause)

Become aware of the body. Be aware of your whole body from the top of your head down to the toes and from the toes up to the crown of your head.

Be aware that your body is resting comfortably. (pause)

Feel stillness in your body.

If at any time you need to move, then move.

Otherwise, you're free to settle in to the comfort you've built for yourself.

Free to settle into your comfortable rest nest. (pause)

Free to do *nothing*. (pause)

Absolute comfort.

Just as you like it.

Just for you.

Effortless. (pause)

Yoga Nidra has now begun. (pause)

Rotation of Consciousness

Now move your awareness into the body – deep into the bones.

Taking an effortless journey throughout the body from point to point.

Freely shifting awareness from one point to the next.

Don't get stuck on any one point.

No need to concentrate, think or analyze.

There's no way to do this incorrectly. (pause)

Simply keep moving awareness swiftly and freely.

Starting by becoming aware of the right side of the body

Become aware of the right hand

Right hand thumb

Index finger

Middle finger

Ring finger

Little finger

Palm of the hand

Back of the hand

Effortless

Right wrist

Lower arm

Elbow

Upper arm

Shoulder

Armpit

Right side of the ribs

Right side of the waist

Hip

Thigh

Knee

Lower leg

Ankle

Heel

Sole of the foot

Top of the foot

Right big toe

Second toe

Third toe

Fourth toe

Fifth toe

Awake and aware

Move awareness to the left side

Become aware of the left hand

Left hand thumb

Index finger

Middle finger

Ring finger

Little finger

Palm of the hand

Back of the hand

Left wrist

Lower arm

Elbow

Upper arm

Shoulder

Armpit

Left side of the ribs

Left side of the waist

Hip

Thigh

Knee

Lower leg

Ankle

Heel

Sole of the foot

Top of the foot

Left big toe

Second toe

Third toe

Fourth toe

Fifth toe

Awake and aware

Move to the crown of the head

Crown of the head

Forehead

Right temple

Left temple

Right eyebrow

Left eyebrow

Eyebrow centre

Sweeping awareness

Right eye

Left eye

Right ear

Left ear

Right cheek

Left cheek

Right nostril

Left nostril

Upper lip

Lower lip

Chin

Throat centre

Right collarbone

Left collarbone

Right side of the chest

Left side of the chest

Heart centre

Navel

Pelvis

Move awareness to the back of the body

Right buttock

Left buttock

Lower back

Middle back

Upper back

Right shoulder blade

Left shoulder blade

Back of the neck

Back of the head

Crown of the head

Move awareness down to the whole right leg

The whole left leg

Both legs together

The whole torso

The whole right arm

The whole left arm

Neck

Head

The whole front of the body

The whole back of the body

Become aware of the whole body together

The whole body together

The whole body together (long pause)

Breath Awareness

Now become aware of the breath in the nostrils. Just as it is. No need to do anything. Simply be aware of the breath. (pause)

Notice the breath coming in like two streams, through the nostrils. (pause)

Feel the streams flowing in along the floor of the nasal passages.

And feel the breath flowing out.

Streams of air flowing in along the floor of the nasal passages.

And streams of air flowing out.

Bring awareness to your right nostril.

Follow the inhalation through your right nostril, and as you exhale, feel it flow out through your left.

Keep awareness on the left nostril as you inhale, and exhale feel the breath flow out through the right.

Mental alternate nostril breathing.

Inhale through the right.

Exhale through the left.

Inhale through the left.

Exhale through the right.

Inhale through the right, count 1.

Exhale through the left, count 2.

Inhale through the left, count 3.

Exhale through the right, count 4.

Keep counting, up to 54.

If you lose track, start again. (pause for 2 minutes) (After 1 minute, say: "Awake and aware.")

Now let go of the count.

Completely let go of the count.

It doesn't matter what number you got to or if the mind wandered.

Simply let go of the count. (pause)

Symbols/Visualization

Shifting to inner wisdom now.

Effortlessly tapping in.

There is an infinite well of knowledge within you. (pause)

A series of symbols will be named.

The mind might or might not spontaneously project images.

There's nothing for you to manifest, search for or think about.

Nothing to do, at all. (pause)

Simply be the witness. As if watching clouds in the sky.

Images or no images, it doesn't matter.

Watching, with detached awareness. (pause)

A green field (repeat 3 times)

A grey elephant (repeat 3 times)

Muddy boots (repeat 3 times)

The pyramids (repeat 3 times)

A mossy rock (repeat 3 times)

A steaming mug (repeat 3 times)

Thick tree roots (repeat 3 times)

A dusty road (repeat 3 times)

Heavy quilt (repeat 3 times)

Starry sky (repeat 3 times)

(pause)

If any insights spontaneously occurred to you, take them with you. If not, that's also fine. Know this time has been useful in awakening your creativity and intuition. (pause)

Externalization

Once again, become aware of the breath.

Be aware that the body is breathing. (pause)

Feel the sensation of your abdomen and chest rising and falling with each breath. (pause)

Feel the sensation of breath through the nostrils. (pause)

Notice the sensation of your body resting – the position of your body… any props under, on, or around your body. (pause)

Notice the texture of any fabric against the skin. (pause)

Notice the temperature of the air on your skin. (pause)

Be aware of the physical body.

Externalize your awareness.

Listening for sounds within the room. (pause)

Become aware of the room you're in – the floor, the walls, the ceiling, the objects in the room. (pause)

Awareness of the room you're in.

Awareness of your body resting comfortably in the room.

Take a deep breath in… bringing awareness back into the body and back into the room. (pause)

Yoga Nidra is now complete. (pause)

Begin to wiggle your fingers and toes. (pause)

Stretch or move your body any way you like. (pause)

And if you're lying down, when you're ready, roll to your right side. (pause)

Take a few deep breaths. (pause)

If you were lying down, press yourself up to sitting. Keep your eyes closed if you can. Take as much time as you need. (pause)

Sitting up, back straight as straight as you can make it, top of the head rising toward the ceiling.

Take a few deep breaths in, feeling the energy start to rise again, yet, feeling grounded and connected to the earth beneath you. (pause)

Feel your connection to the earth beneath you. Stable and secure. (pause)

We'll finish by chanting Om and Shanti, three times each.

Om is a universal mantra, and Shanti means peace.

Om Om Om Shanti Shanti Shanti (pause)

When you're ready, softly, slowly open your eyes. Adjusting back into the room, back into your day, refreshed and grounded.

Balancing Yoga Nidra *(30-35 min.)*

Discover your natural state of balance, the peaceful, harmonious state that is your birthright.

<u>Suggested Pre- and Post-Practices:</u>

- Asana practice before this balancing Yoga Nidra practice will depend on the students' need. If students have an abundance of rajas (busy lifestyle, active mind) then an active asana class that progressively gets slower can be beneficial to bring them back to balance (sattva). If students have an abundance of tamas (inactive, lethargic), then a class that begins slowly and progressively gets more engaging can bring them back to balance (sattva).

- Prepare or finish with a few minutes of Samana Mudra for calming the mind and balancing elemental energies.

Settling

Getting comfortable for this balancing Yoga Nidra practice – lying on your back or if it's not comfortable, lying on your side, or sitting up, supported.

Maybe making a cozy rest nest with cushions, blankets, bolsters, eye pillow – whatever your body needs to feel as comfortable as possible in this moment. (pause)

Getting ready to do nothing. (pause)

This time is just for you.

This practice is just for you.

There are no shoulds or shouldn'ts.

There's no way you can do this wrong.

This is about you.

This is for you.

So make yourself as comfortable as you like, in just the way you like.

Adjusting anything you like. In any way you like.

Listening in to what you need. And then answering that request.

You might prefer a lot of cushions, blankets and props, you might prefer just a few, you might even prefer none. All are equally welcome.

Do whatever you need feel supported, held, and free to let go of tensions.

Getting comfortable for this practice of non-doing.

Check in with how you feel.

Your set-up should make you feel at ease, but not sleepy.

If you do feel sleepy, you could make it slightly less warm, slightly less dark.

You can also check your head position. If your chin is tucked in, it can stimulate sleep. Try moving your head into a neutral alignment, chin neither tucked nor raised, and notice how it might change your energy and alertness. Try moving your head into a position where you feel relaxed yet still alert, not sleepy. (pause)

Set yourself up so you can stay awake and aware, and at the same time, in peaceful ease.

Beginning a check now that each body part is as relaxed as can be. If you can't completely relax, that's fine. You're welcome just as you are.

Check that your feet and ankles are relaxed as can be. (pause)

Calves, knees and thighs relaxed as can be. (pause)

Hips relaxed as can be. (pause)

Lower back, middle back, upper back releasing tension. Whole back, melting. (pause)

Hands and arms letting go. (pause)

Shoulders and neck melting, tension diffusing. (pause)

Jaw, tongue and cheeks softening. (pause)

Eyes, forehead and scalp softening. (pause)

Whole body melting into the support of the earth beneath you. Held by the support of the earth beneath you. (pause)

Nothing for you to do. (pause)

Body is supported and resting. (pause)

Awareness continues on. (pause)

Yoga Nidra has now begun. (pause)

Rotation of Consciousness

Now beginning the process of sweeping awareness and energy throughout the body.

Moving from one point to the next, you can visualize the point physically, as a point of light, sensing energetically or in any way that feels right.

Move awareness over to the right hand

Right hand thumb

Index finger

Middle finger

Ring finger

Little finger

Physical awareness, point of light, energy or other experience

Moving over to the left hand thumb

Index finger

Middle finger

Ring finger

Little finger

And now over to the right wrist

Left wrist

Right elbow

Left elbow

Sweeping awareness, sweeping energy

Right shoulder

Left shoulder

Hollow of the throat

Back of the head near the top

Crown of the head

Eyebrow centre

Right eyebrow

Left eyebrow

Right eye

Left eye

Right ear

Left ear

Right cheek

Left cheek

Tip of the nose

Upper lip

Lower lip

Chin

Hollow of the throat

Heart centre

Right side of the chest

Heart centre

Left side of the chest

Heart centre

Navel centre

Tip of the tailbone

Right hip

Left hip

Right knee

Left knee

Right ankle

Left ankle

Right big toe

Second toe

Third toe

Fourth toe

Little toe

Left big toe

Second toe

Third toe

Fourth toe

Little toe

The whole right side of the body

The whole left side of the body

The whole body together

The whole body together

The whole body together

Breath Awareness

Now become aware of the breath in the nostrils. Just as it is. No need to do anything.

Simply be aware of the breath.

Notice the breath coming in like two streams, through the nostrils.

Feel the streams flowing in along the floor of the nasal passages.

And feel the breath flowing out.

Streams of air flowing in along the floor of the nasal passages.

And streams of air flowing out. (pause)

Bring awareness to your right nostril.

Follow the inhalation through your right nostril, and as you exhale, feel it flow out through your left nostril.

Keep awareness on the left nostril as you inhale, and exhale feel the breath flow out through the right nostril.

Mental alternate nostril breathing.

Inhale through the right.

Exhale through the left.

Inhale through the left.

Exhale through the right.

Inhale through the right, count 1.

Exhale through the left, count 2.

Inhale through the left, count 3.

Exhale through the right, count 4.

Keep counting, up to 54.

If you lose track, start again. (pause for 2 minutes) (After 1 minute, say: "Awake and aware.")

Now let go of the count. It doesn't matter what number you got to or if the mind wandered.

Let go of the count completely.

Breathing normally. (pause)

As you exhale, feel that you let go of any fatigue, stress, tension.

As you inhale, feel that you're pulling in *boundless energy*.

Exhale letting go of fatigue, stress, tension.

Inhale pulling in boundless energy.

Exhale letting go.

Inhale energy.

Now exhale from the crown of the head down to the toes, tension out.

Inhale from the toes up to the crown of the head, energy in.

Exhale from the crown of the head down to the ankles.

Inhale from the ankles up to the crown of the head.

Exhale from the crown of the head down to the knees.

Inhale from the knees up to the crown of the head.

Exhale from the crown down the spine to the tailbone.

Inhale from the tailbone up the spine to the crown.

Exhale from the crown down the spine to the navel.

Inhale from the navel up the spine to the crown.

Exhale from the crown down the spine to the heart centre.

Inhale from the heart centre up the spine to the crown.

Exhale from the crown down to the throat centre.

Inhale from the throat centre up the spine to the crown.

Exhale from the crown down to the bridge between the nostrils.

Inhale from the bridge between the nostrils up to the crown.

Now to the third eye, exhale down to the bridge between the nostrils.

Inhale from the bridge between the nostrils, up to the third eye.

Back to the crown, exhale down to the bridge between the nostrils.

Inhale from the bridge between the nostrils up to the crown.

Exhale from the crown down the spine to the throat centre.

Inhale from the throat centre up the spine to the crown.

Exhale from the crown down the spine to the heart centre.

Inhale from the heart centre up the spine to the crown.

Exhale from the crown down the spine to the navel.

Inhale from the navel up the spine to the crown.

Exhale from the crown down the spine to the tailbone.

Inhale from the tailbone up the spine to the crown.

Exhale from the crown of the head down to the knees.

Inhale from the knees up to the crown of the head.

Exhale from the crown of the head down to the ankles.

Inhale from the ankles up to the crown of the head.

Exhale from the crown of head down to the toes.

Inhale from the toes up to the crown of the head. (pause)

Feel that the whole body is breathing in and out. (pause)

Inhaling cosmic energy from all around you, exhaling any fatigue, tension, energy blocks. (long pause)

Opposites

Now beginning to manifest sensations in the body.

Start by developing the feeling of heaviness.

Each part of your body becoming heavier and heavier.

Heavy like stone.

Feel the right leg heavy like stone, sinking into the surface beneath you.

Left leg becoming heavier and heavier. Sinking down… so heavy you couldn't lift it.

Now feel heaviness in the hips… back… chest… The whole torso is sinking into the surface beneath you. So heavy.

Shoulders now sinking. Heaviness extending down the arms and to the hands. Hands heavy like stone.

Head heavy, sinking down into the surface beneath you.

Manifesting the sensation of heaviness in the whole body.

Entire body heavy like stone. (pause)

Now let go of the sensation of heaviness.

Completely let it go.

Release the sensation of heaviness from every part of the body.

Now awaken the sensation of lightness in the body.

Feel that every part of the body is filling up with lightness like a helium balloon.

Body becoming lighter and lighter.

The right leg becoming light, lifting up.

Left leg filling up with lightness and floating right up.

The right arm becoming lighter and lighter, picking up.

The left arm becoming light, floating up.

The hips and torso becoming light, filling up like a helium balloon, and floating right up.

And finally the head, filling with the sensation of lightness, floating right up.

Entire body, floating. Light as air.

Experience lightness throughout the entire body.

Absolute lightness. (pause)

Now let go of the sensation of lightness.

Allow your body to gently release the feeling of floating.

Completely let go of the sensation of lightness.

Now manifesting the sensation of cold in the body.

Start by feeling the sensation of a cool breeze blowing across your whole body.

Cool breeze – from the tips of your toes to the top of your head, and from the top of your head to the tips of your toes. (pause)

Feel your whole body naturally contracting, pulling in from the cold – deep in until your body shivers.

Cold permeating your skin… tissues… deep into your bones.

Goosebumps across your body. Shivering.

Feel cold in all parts of the body – cold in the arms, cold legs, cold torso, head. Feel the cold on your face – cheeks, tip of your nose, forehead. Cold at your temples, up along the back of your neck, shivering, cold at the top of your head.

Cold and shivering, throughout the whole body. (pause)

Now let go of the sensation of cold.

Completely let it go.

Let go of the sensation of cold throughout the whole body.

Now manifesting the sensation of heat in the body.

Feel heat arising in the whole body.

Heat, like a sweltering summer day. Heat on your skin, arms, legs, fingers, toes, face.

Getting hotter and hotter.

Heat radiating through every pore of your body.

So much heat, sweat is escaping from your pores.

Feel your whole body breaking out in a sweat. Armpits sweating, forehead sweating, eyelids sweating, palms sweating, soles of the feet, hot and sweating. Heat throughout the entire body. (pause)

Hot and sweating throughout the whole body. (pause)

Now let go of the sensation of heat.

Completely let it go.

Let go of the sensation of heat throughout the whole body. (pause)

If you were able to manifest any of these sensations, notice what happened when you let it go. When you let go, the state of balance reveals itself.

Balance is always there, waiting behind the opposites. Balance is your natural state. Always there for you, beneath the opposites of heavy/light, hot/cold, energized & tired, busy & stuck.

Balance is your natural state.

Balance is your default mode.

Let go of the opposites and balance appears.

That state of balance is here for you, anytime you like.

It is yours.

Letting go, you arrive at your natural state of balance. (pause)

Taking a few minutes now, simply resting.

Nothing to do.

Simply resting. (pause for 1-3 minutes)

Externalization

Ommmmmm Ommmmmm Ommmmmm

Bringing awareness back to the breath. Notice your body breathing. Feel your body breathing. Take a moment to enjoy the non-doing of your breathing. (pause)

Now take a deep breath.

Feel energy and awareness coming back into the body. (pause)

Yoga Nidra is now complete. (pause)

Take another breath. (pause)

And if you feel like making gentle movements in the body, make them. If you feel like making larger movements, make them.

Listening in and moving when and how you'd like. (pause)

If you like, take a moment to recall your experience. What will you take with you from your experience today? (pause)

Make your way to sitting upright.

Keep the eyes closed if you can.

Feel the energy rising upward as you sit. (pause)

Feel the body activating.

The mind activating.

And yet, still remaining relaxed.

Possibly feeling more balanced than when you began. Maybe more rested, or peaceful.

Taking a moment to enjoy any positive experience from your Yoga Nidra practice today. (pause)

Thanking yourself for simply being here. Thanking yourself for taking this time for yourself. (pause)

I'll finish by chanting Om and Shanti three times each. Join in if you like.

Notice your energy rising with the chant.

Om Om Om Shanti Shanti Shanti (pause)

And slowly, softly opening your eyes, bringing any balanced sensation with you, into the room and into your day.

Shifting Seasons Yoga Nidra – Winter to Spring *(35 min.)*

Synchronize with the rhythm of nature and shift beautifully from the season of rest and reflection to the season of rebirth.

Suggested Pre- and Post-Practices:

- Begin with a relaxed asana or movement practice that loosens up the joints and major muscles.

- Begin or finish with a few minutes of holding Abhaya Mudra for fearlessness in shifting into rebirth.

- Prepare or finish with a Shanti Mantra such as:

  > Sarvesham svastir bhavatu
  >
  > Sarvesham shantir bhavatu
  >
  > Sarvesham purnam bhavatu
  >
  > Sarvesham mangalam bhavatu

  (May prosperity be unto all, may peace be unto all, may fullness be unto all, may auspiciousness be unto all)

- Finish with kapalabhati breathing and self-massage on the shoulders, back of the neck, scalp, arms, legs and soles of the feet.

Settling

Find yourself a comfortable place to lie down, or if you prefer, a place to sit up, supported.

Getting ready for this Yoga Nidra practice to help you shift beautifully into the season of rebirth. (pause)

107

Have a thin pillow or blanket tucked comfortably under your head. (pause)

Cover yourself with a blanket if you like. (pause)

Do anything you need to do to become as comfortable as possible. (long pause)

Set aside anything that's on your mind. Right now, there's nothing you need to do. Set everything aside for this time to connect within. (pause)

If you're lying in savasana, legs are apart. Feet flopped out to the sides. Your arms are away from the body, leaving space beneath the armpits. Palms are facing up. (pause)

In any position, shoulders are away from the ears. (pause)

Check that your neck is in line and feeling comfortable. (pause)

Check for any lumps or bumps of clothing, jewellery, or the surface beneath you that might draw your attention away. If you find any, adjust them now. (pause)

Scan your whole body, checking that you're as comfortable as can be and that there's nothing calling your attention – nothing that might draw your attention away from your practice of Yoga Nidra. (pause)

Take a deep breath in… and a long breath out.

Take another deep breath in, and as you exhale, feel yourself settle, and let go. (pause)

Now is the time to make any final adjustments you need so you can be still for your Yoga Nidra practice. (pause)

Make sure you're completely comfortable and can completely surrender all doing.

Know that you can move whenever you need to, but make yourself so comfortable you'll have absolutely no desire to move. (pause)

Begin to feel the stillness. Rest in that stillness. (pause)

Become aware of distant sounds. (long pause)

Allow your sense of hearing to extend out, receiving all sounds effortlessly and without analysis. Simply receiving with effortless awareness. (pause)

Now bring your hearing into the room. Receiving sounds within the room. (pause)

Listen for the soft sound of your own body breathing. (pause)

Feel the body resting. (pause)

Be aware of your body breathing.

Your body breathing itself. (pause)

Nothing to do. (pause)

No need for concentration. Just effortless awareness. (pause)

Say to yourself mentally, "I'm going to practice Yoga Nidra." (pause) "I will remain awake and aware." (pause)

Yoga Nidra has now begun. (pause)

Sankalpa

With a focus on shifting into the spring season, know that spring is arriving.

Feel that spring is arriving. (pause)

All of nature is waking up, rested and renewed, ready to spring forth in beautiful new ways. (pause)

Sunshine making a glorious re-appearance… plants sprouting up… birds' eggs hatching. (pause)

All of life is new. (pause)

And you can emerge in a radiant new form, too. (pause)

Re-energized and fresh. (pause)

Picture yourself effortlessly following this spring rhythm of nature. (pause)

The season of rest is ending and the season of rebirth is arising. (pause)

Without *any* fear, allowing yourself to imagine change for yourself. (pause)

Leave behind any old ideas or behaviours that feel heavy. (pause)

What will you leave behind? (pause)

Allowing space for your metamorphosis. (pause)

Knowing that it's perfectly natural to follow the rhythm of change right now.

Embracing the potential in change. Opportunity for new experiences… new perspectives… new learning… new growth. (pause)

New levels of joy, peace and knowledge. (pause)

Picture yourself being reborn, re-invented. (pause)

What will it look like? (pause) Sound like? (pause) Feel like? (pause)

Allow your heart to lead the way. *Feel* into it. (pause)

Know that your heart's desires will be amplified by the energy of the spring season.

It is the ideal season to renew momentum.

Setting an intention for spring, say to yourself mentally now,

I shift *beautifully* into the season of *rebirth*. (pause)

I shift beautifully into the season of rebirth. (pause)

I shift beautifully into the season of rebirth. (pause)

Rotation of Consciousness

Now taking a trip through the body, witnessing with curiosity and effortless awareness.

Allow the mind to hop from one body part to the next.

No need to think. Just awareness.

Awareness of any sensations, thoughts or feelings that might arise, but without attachment.

Simply noticing, and moving freely on.

Bring awareness to the point between the eyebrows

The point between the eyebrows

The hollow of the throat

The right shoulder

The right elbow

Effortless travelling deep in the body

Down to the middle of the right wrist

The right thumb

The tip of the index finger

Tip of the middle finger

Tip of the ring finger

Tip of the little finger

Back up to the right wrist

The elbow

The shoulder

The hollow of the throat

Sweeping awareness over to the left shoulder

Down to the left elbow

Deep in the body, effortless

The middle of the left wrist

The left thumb

Tip of the index finger

Tip of the middle finger

Tip of the ring finger

Tip of the little finger

Back up to the left wrist

The elbow

The shoulder

The hollow of the throat

The heart centre

The right side of the chest

The heart centre

The left side of the chest

The heart centre

The navel centre

Tip of the tailbone

The right hip joint

The right knee joint

The ankle joint

The right big toe

Tip of the second toe

Tip of the third toe

Tip of the fourth toe

Tip of the baby toe

Back up to the right ankle joint

Knee joint

Hip joint

Tip of the tailbone

Sweeping awareness to the left hip joint

Left knee joint

Ankle joint

The left big toe

Tip of the second toe

Tip of the third toe

Tip of the fourth toe

Tip of the baby toe

Back up to the left ankle

Knee joint

Hip joint

Tip of the tailbone

Navel centre

Heart centre

Hollow of the throat

The eyebrow centre

The eyebrow centre

The eyebrow centre (pause)

Breath Awareness

Now become aware of the chest.

Notice the body breathing itself. (pause)

Chest gently rises and falls with each breath. (pause)

Nothing for you to do.

Simply witnessing. (pause)

Now bring awareness to the nostrils. (pause)

Without making any changes to the breath, feel that the breath is coming in from far away in two separate streams, through the nostrils.

Two streams coming in through the nostrils and meeting at the point between the eyebrows.

Two streams, coming in from afar, through the nostrils, to meet at the point between the eyebrows, the third eye.

Keep breathing in this way, two streams from afar, meeting at the point between the eyebrows, the eye of intuition. (pause)

Feel the third eye centre with each breath.

Locate it behind the centre between the eyebrows, in the centre of the brain.

Behind the centre between the eyebrows, in the centre of the brain.

This is the centre for intuitive knowing.

As you bring awareness to the third eye, you bring energy, *prana*.

Where the awareness goes, energy flows. (pause)

Continue to breathe in this way, counting down from 16 to 1.

Inhale to the third eye 16

Exhale 15

Inhale to the third eye 14

Exhale 13

And so on, down to 1. If you lose track, start again. If you finish, start again. (30s. pause)

Now let go of the count.

It doesn't matter what number you got to, or if you lost track.

Letting go of the count. (pause)

Opposites

Now beginning to manifest sensations in the body.

Start by developing the feeling of heaviness.

Each part of your body becoming heavier and heavier.

Heavy, like lead.

Feel the right leg heavy like lead, sinking, into the surface beneath you.

Left leg becoming heavier and heavier. Sinking down... so heavy you couldn't lift it.

Now feel heaviness in hips... back... chest... The whole torso is sinking into the surface beneath you. So heavy.

Shoulders now sinking. Heaviness extending down the arms and to the hands. Hands heavy, like lead.

Head heavy, sinking down into the surface beneath you.

Manifesting the sensation of heaviness in the whole body.

Entire body heavy like lead. (pause)

Now let go of the sensation of heaviness.

Completely let it go.

Release the sensation of heaviness from every part of the body.

Now awaken the sensation of lightness in the body.

Feel that every part of the body is filling up with lightness, like a helium balloon.

Body becoming lighter and lighter.

The right leg becoming light, lifting up.

Left leg filling up with lightness and floating right up.

The right arm becoming lighter and lighter, picking up.

The left arm becoming light, floating up.

The hips and torso becoming light, filling up, like a helium balloon, and floating right up.

And finally the head, filling with the sensation of lightness, floating right up.

Entire body, floating up. Light as air.

Experience lightness throughout the entire body.

Absolute lightness. (pause)

Now let go of the sensation of lightness.

Allow your body to gently release the feeling of floating.

Completely let go of the sensation of lightness.

Notice you can manifest or let go of the sensations of heaviness and lightness, any time you need. (pause)

Symbols/Visualization

Now beginning the process of allowing the subconscious mind to open, and creativity to flow forth.

A series of symbols will be named. Images, thoughts or feelings might arise.

Continue to be the witness. Effortless.

Simply watching, with detached awareness. (pause)

A pink scarf (repeat 3 times)

Bowl of berries (repeat 3 times)

Dusty books (repeat 3 times)

Morning sunlight (repeat 3 times)

Evergreen tree (repeat 3 times)

Raindrops on a window (repeat 3 times)

Fluffy mittens (repeat 3 times)

Railway track (repeat 3 times)

Red bricks (repeat 3 times)

Blue sky (repeat 3 times)

(pause)

Sankalpa

Now is the perfect time to repeat your spring intention again. If you repeat it with feeling and awareness now, it cannot fail. Say to yourself mentally,

I shift *beautifully* into the season of *rebirth*. (pause)

I shift beautifully into the season of rebirth. (pause)

I shift beautifully into the season of rebirth. (pause)

Know that your intention has been received deep in your being and is already manifesting. Take a moment to feel the joy of your intention manifested. (pause)

Externalization

Become aware of your breath. (pause)

Your body resting, breathing itself. (pause)

Listen for the soft sound of your body breathing. (pause)

Feel the sensation of your body breathing. (pause)

Externalizing your awareness.

Become aware of the room you're in, floor, walls, ceiling. Listen for sounds within the room. (pause)

Know that the practice of Yoga Nidra is coming to an end.

Develop awareness of your body and the place you're in.

Feel your awareness coming back into the body.

Yoga Nidra is now complete. (pause)

Beginning gentle movements in the body, wiggle your fingers. Wiggle your toes.

Make any gentle movements with the body that feel good. (pause)

Now make any larger movements – move your feet, legs, hands, arms, move any body parts that are calling you, and if you're lying down, when you're ready, roll to the right side. (pause)

Take a few deep breaths, recalling anything that spoke to you in your Yoga Nidra practice today. (pause)

If you were lying down, press yourself slowly up to sitting. Keep your eyes closed if you can. Take your time, there's no rush. (pause)

Sitting comfortably, back as straight as you can make it.

Take a deep breath in… and a long breath out.

Say to yourself mentally one more time:

"I shift beautifully into the season of rebirth." (pause)

We'll finish by chanting Om and Shanti, three times each.

Om Om Om Shanti Shanti Shanti (pause)

Hold the feeling of shifting beautifully into the season of rebirth, as you softly open your eyes. Allow your eyes and your awareness to adjust back into the room and back into your day.

Shifting Seasons Yoga Nidra – Spring to Summer *(35 min.)*

Synchronize with the rhythm of nature and shift beautifully from the season of rebirth to the season of action.

Suggested Pre- and Post-Practices:

- Begin with a few sun salutations to loosen up the body.

- Also consider finishing with some energizing sun salutations or asanas, to stimulate the move into action immediately.

- Finish with a few minutes of Prana Mudra to harness the energy needed to spring into action.

- Prepare or finish with a Shanti Mantra such as:

    Sarvesham svastir bhavatu

    Sarvesham shantir bhavatu

    Sarvesham purnam bhavatu

    Sarvesham mangalam bhavatu

    (May prosperity be unto all, may peace be unto all, may fullness be unto all, may auspiciousness be unto all)

Settling

Find yourself a comfortable place to lie down, or if you prefer, a place to sit up, supported.

Getting ready for this Yoga Nidra practice, to help you shift beautifully into the season of action. (pause)

119

Have a thin pillow or blanket tucked comfortably under your head. (pause)

Cover yourself with a blanket if you like. (pause)

Do anything you need to do to get as comfortable as possible. (long pause)

Set aside anything that's on your mind. Right now, there's nothing you need to do. (pause)

Set everything aside for this time to connect within. (pause)

If you're lying in savasana, legs are apart. Feet flopped out to the sides. Your arms are away from the body, leaving space beneath the armpits. Palms are facing up. (pause)

In any position, shoulders are away from the ears. (pause)

Check that your neck is in line and feeling comfortable. (pause)

Check for any lumps or bumps of clothing, jewellery, or the surface beneath you that might draw your attention away. If you find any, adjust them now. (pause)

Scan your whole body, checking that you're as comfortable as can be and that there's nothing calling your attention – nothing that might draw your attention away from your Yoga Nidra practice. (pause)

Take a deep breath in… and a long breath out.

Take another deep breath in and as you exhale, feel yourself settle, and let go. (pause)

Now is the time to make any final adjustments you need so you can be still for your Yoga Nidra practice. (pause)

Make sure you're completely comfortable and can completely surrender all doing.

Know that you can move whenever you need to, but make yourself so comfortable you'll have absolutely no desire to move. (pause)

Begin to feel the stillness. Rest in that stillness. (pause)

Become aware of distant sounds. (pause)

Allow your sense of hearing to extend out, receiving all sounds effortlessly and without analysis. Simply receiving all sounds, with effortless awareness. (long pause)

Now bring your hearing into the room. Receiving any sounds within the room. (pause)

Listen for the sound of your own body breathing. (pause)

Feel the body resting. (pause)

Be aware of your body breathing.

Your body breathing itself. (pause)

Nothing to do. (pause)

No need for concentration. Just effortless awareness. (pause)

Say to yourself mentally, "I'm going to practice Yoga Nidra." (pause) "I will remain awake and aware."

Yoga Nidra has now begun. (pause)

Sankalpa

With a focus on shifting into the summer season, know that summer is arriving.

Feel that summer is arriving. (pause)

All of nature in full bloom and at the height of potential.

Animals are playing, the air is sweet, the sun is radiant and energizing.

It's the perfect time for you to play, too.

Time to dance with this summer rhythm.

Full of life, playful, productive.

Test out your shiny new wings.

See what you can do – soar to new heights, fly off and explore, try some new tricks. The sky is the limit and the sky is all clear for takeoff.

Without any fear, any self-doubt, allow yourself to take flight, take action on your dreams.

There is no better time.

The sun is energizing your every move.

Casting you in gorgeous, radiant light.

The birds are singing your song.

The air is fresh. All of nature is pulsing with life.

All of nature is conspiring to help you fully bloom, into your highest expression of potential.

Vibrant, strong and sublimely stunning.

Setting a summer intention now, say to yourself mentally,

I shift *beautifully* into the season of *action*. (pause)

I shift beautifully into the season of action. (pause)

I shift beautifully into the season of action. (pause)

Rotation of Consciousness

Now taking your awareness on a trip through the body. Effortless. Like a traveller on vacation.

Allow your awareness to hop from one body part to the next.

No need to think. Just awareness.

Awareness of any sensations, thoughts, feelings that might arise, but without attachment.

Simply noticing and moving freely on.

Bring awareness to the point between the eyebrows

The point between the eyebrows

The hollow of the throat

The right shoulder

The right elbow

Effortless travelling, deep in the body

Down to the middle of the right wrist

The right thumb

The tip of the index finger

Tip of the middle finger

Tip of the ring finger

Tip of the little finger

Back up to the right wrist

The elbow

The shoulder

The hollow of the throat

Sweeping awareness over to the left shoulder

Down to the left elbow

Deep in the body, effortless

The middle of the left wrist

The left thumb

Tip of the index finger

Tip of the middle finger

Tip of the ring finger

Tip of the little finger

Back up to the left wrist

The elbow

The shoulder

The hollow of the throat

The heart centre

The right side of the chest

The heart centre

The left side of the chest

The heart centre

The navel centre

Tip of the tailbone

The right hip joint

The right knee joint

The ankle joint

The right big toe

Tip of the second toe

Tip of the third toe

Tip of the fourth toe

Tip of the baby toe

Back up to the right ankle joint

Knee joint

Hip joint

Tip of the tailbone

Sweeping awareness to the left hip joint

Left knee joint

Ankle joint

The left big toe

Tip of the second toe

Tip of the third toe

Tip of the fourth toe

Tip of the baby toe

Back up to the left ankle

Knee joint

Hip joint

Tip of the tailbone

Navel centre

Heart centre

Hollow of the throat

The eyebrow centre

The eyebrow centre

The eyebrow centre (pause)

Breath Awareness

Now beginning with breath awareness.

Become aware of the navel centre. (pause)

Notice the abdomen gently rising and falling with each breath. (pause)

Notice the body is breathing itself.

Nothing for you to do.

Simply witnessing. (pause)

Keep keen awareness at the navel centre. (pause)

The navel centre is your centre for vitality. For personal fire. (pause)

As you bring awareness to the navel centre, you fuel it with life force.

Where your awareness goes, energy flows.

Keep awareness at the navel centre, your centre for personal power. Keen, but relaxed.

Without making any changes to the breath, feel as if the breath is being pulled in, down to the navel centre. (pause)

Energy coming in with each breath, fuelling the powerhouse at your navel. (pause)

Fanning the flames of your vitality. (pause)

Continue to breathe in this way, counting down from 16 to 1.

Inhale to the navel 16

Exhale 15

Inhale to the navel 14

Exhale 13

And so on, down to 1. If you lose track, start again. If you finish, start again. (30s. pause)

Now let go of the count.

It doesn't matter what number you got to, or if you lost track.

Letting go of the count. (pause)

Opposites

Now beginning to manifest sensations in the body.

Start by developing the feeling of heaviness.

Each part of your body becoming heavier and heavier. Heavy, like lead.

Feel the right leg heavy like lead, sinking into the surface beneath you.

Left leg becoming heavier and heavier. Sinking down… so heavy you couldn't lift it.

Now feel heaviness in hips… back… chest… The whole torso sinking into the surface beneath you. So heavy.

Shoulders now sinking. Heaviness extending down the arms and to the hands. Hands heavy like lead.

Head heavy, sinking down into the surface beneath you.

Manifesting the sensation of heaviness in the whole body.

Entire body heavy, like lead. (pause)

Now let go of the sensation of heaviness.

Completely let it go.

Release the sensation of heaviness from every part of the body. (pause)

Now awaken the sensation of lightness in the body.

Feel that every part of the body is filling up with lightness, like a helium balloon.

Body becoming lighter and lighter.

The right leg becoming light, lifting up.

Left leg filling up with lightness and floating right up.

The right arm becoming lighter and lighter, picking up.

The left arm becoming light, floating up.

The hips and torso becoming light, filling up like a helium balloon, and floating right up.

And finally the head, filling with the sensation of lightness, floating right up.

Entire body, floating up. Light as air.

Experience lightness throughout the entire body.

Absolute lightness. (pause)

Now let go of the sensation of lightness.

Allow your body to gently release the feeling of floating.

Completely let go of the sensation of lightness. (pause)

Notice you can manifest or let go of the sensations of heaviness and lightness, any time you need. (pause)

Symbols/Visualization

Now beginning the process of accessing the subconscious mind. Allowing the doors of creativity to open.

A series of symbols will be named. Images, thoughts or feelings might arise.

Continue to be the witness. Effortless.

Simply watching, with detached awareness. (pause)

A white hat (repeat 3 times)

Bowl of cherries (repeat 3 times)

Newspaper (repeat 3 times)

Blazing sun (repeat 3 times)

Blue paint (repeat 3 times)

Light reflected on the water (repeat 3 times)

Ice cubes (repeat 3 times)

Hairbrush (repeat 3 times)

Chandelier (repeat 3 times)

Rainbow (repeat 3 times)

(pause)

Sankalpa

Now is the perfect time to repeat your intention for summer. If you repeat it with feeling and awareness now, it cannot fail. Say to yourself mentally,

I shift *beautifully* into the season of *action*. (pause)

I shift beautifully into the season of action. (pause)

I shift beautifully into the season of action. (pause)

Know that your intention has been received deep in your being and is already manifesting. Take a moment to feel the joy of this intention manifested. (pause)

Externalization

Become aware of your breath. (pause)

Your body resting, breathing itself. (pause)

Hear the sound of your body breathing. (pause)

Feel the sensation of your body breathing. (pause)

Externalizing your awareness.

Become aware of the room you're in, floor, walls, ceiling. Listen for sounds within the room. (pause)

Know that the practice of Yoga Nidra is coming to an end.

Develop awareness of your body and the place you're in.

Feel your awareness coming back into the body.

Yoga Nidra is now complete. (pause)

Beginning gentle movements in the body, wiggle your fingers. Wiggle your toes.

Make any gentle movements with the body that feel good. (pause)

Now make any larger movements – move your feet, legs, hands, arms, move any body parts that are calling you, and if you're lying down, when you're ready, roll to the right side.

Take a few deep breaths, recalling anything that spoke to you from your Yoga Nidra practice today. (pause)

If you were lying down, press yourself slowly up to sitting. Keep your eyes closed if you can. Take your time, there's no rush. (pause)

Sitting comfortably, back as straight as you can make it.

Take a deep breath in… and a long breath out.

Say to yourself mentally one more time:

"I shift beautifully into the season of action." (pause)

We'll finish by chanting Om and Shanti, three times each.

Om Om Om Shanti Shanti Shanti (pause)

Hold the feeling of shifting beautifully into action as you softly open your eyes.

Allow your eyes and your awareness to adjust back into the room and into the rest of your day.

Shifting Seasons Yoga Nidra – Summer to Fall *(35 min.)*

Synchronize with the rhythm of nature and shift beautifully from the season of action to the season of letting go.

Suggested Pre- and Post-Practices:

- Since this practice helps to shift from the season of action to the season of letting go, a slower asana practice that helps to deeply stretch and let go of tensions would be a great fit.

- Prepare or finish with Anjali Mudra, for the humility to let go.

- Prepare or finish with a Shanti Mantra such as:

    Sarvesham svastir bhavatu

    Sarvesham shantir bhavatu

    Sarvesham purnam bhavatu

    Sarvesham mangalam bhavatu

    (May prosperity be unto all, may peace be unto all, may fullness be unto all, may auspiciousness be unto all)

Settling

Find yourself a comfortable place to lie down, or if you prefer, a place to sit up, supported. (pause)

Getting ready for your Yoga Nidra practice, to help you transition beautifully from the season of action to the season of letting go. (pause)

Have a thin pillow or blanket tucked comfortably under your head. (pause)

Cover yourself with a blanket if you like. (pause)

Set aside anything that's on your mind. Right now, there's nothing you need to do. Set everything aside for this time to connect within. (pause)

If you're lying in savasana, legs are apart. Feet flopped out to the sides. Your arms are away from the body, leaving space beneath the armpits. Palms are facing up. (pause)

In any position, shoulders are away from the ears. (pause)

Check that your neck is in line and feeling comfortable. (pause)

Check for any lumps or bumps of clothing, jewellery, or the surface beneath you that might draw your attention away. If you find any, adjust them now. (pause)

Scan your whole body, checking that you're as comfortable as can be and that there's nothing calling your attention – nothing that might draw your attention away from this practice of Yoga Nidra. (long pause)

Take a deep breath in… and a long breath out.

Take another deep breath in and as you exhale, feel yourself settle, and let go.

Now is the time to make any final adjustments you need, so you're completely comfortable and can completely surrender all doing.

Know that you can move whenever you need to, but make yourself so comfortable you'll have absolutely no desire to move. (pause)

Begin to feel that stillness. Rest in that stillness. (pause)

Become aware of distant sounds. (long pause)

Allow your sense of hearing to extend out, receiving all sounds effortlessly and without analysis. Simply receiving with effortless awareness. (pause)

Now bring your hearing into the room. Receiving any sounds within the room. (pause)

Now listen for the soft sound of your own body breathing. (pause)

Feel the body resting. (pause)

Be aware of your body breathing.

Your body breathing itself. (pause)

Nothing to do.

No need for concentration. Just effortless awareness.

Say to yourself mentally, "I'm going to practice Yoga Nidra." (pause) "I will remain awake and aware."

Yoga Nidra has now begun. (pause)

Sankalpa

With a focus on shifting into the fall season, know that fall is arriving.

Feel that fall is arriving. (pause)

Notice the trees are releasing their leaves, in one final, gorgeous grand finale.

Give *yourself* permission to let go, too. (pause)

Make way for whatever new beauty is waiting in the wings. (pause)

Picture yourself effortlessly following this fall rhythm of nature.

Letting go of anything you no longer need, with grace and beauty. (pause)

Bidding adieu to old mindsets or habits. (pause)

Letting go of your busy schedule, making way for some well-earned downtime. (pause)

Without *any* guilt, letting go. (pause)

Knowing that it's perfectly natural to let go right now.

Embracing the joy of letting go. The freedom, the lightness, the cleared slate ready for you to create your next masterpiece. (pause)

Picture yourself letting go. What will you release? A thought? A feeling? A habit? An activity? Not thinking, just feeling into it. What would you like to release? (pause)

What spontaneously comes to mind first? (pause)

Picture yourself after it's been released. (pause)

Feel the lightness of that release. (pause)

Setting a fall intention, say to yourself mentally now,

I shift *beautifully* into the season of *letting go*. (pause)

I shift beautifully into the season of letting go. (pause)

I shift beautifully into the season of letting go. (pause)

Rotation of Consciousness

Now taking a trip through the body, witnessing with curiosity and effortless awareness.

Allow the mind to hop from one body part to the next.

No need to think. Just awareness.

Awareness of any sensations, thoughts, feelings that might arise, but without attachment.

Simply noticing and moving freely on.

Bring awareness to the point between the eyebrows

The hollow of the throat

The right shoulder

The right elbow

Effortless travelling deep in the body

Down to the middle of the right wrist

The right thumb

The tip of the index finger

Tip of the middle finger

Tip of the ring finger

Tip of the little finger

Back up to the wrist

The elbow

The shoulder

The hollow of the throat

Sweeping awareness over to the left shoulder

Down to the left elbow

Deep in the body, effortless

The middle of the left wrist

The left thumb

Tip of the index finger

Tip of the middle finger

Tip of the ring finger

Tip of the little finger

Back up to the wrist

The elbow

The shoulder

The hollow of the throat

The heart centre

The right side of the chest

The heart centre

The left side of the chest

The heart centre

The navel centre

Tip of the tailbone

The right hip joint

The right knee joint

The ankle joint

The right big toe

Tip of the second toe

Tip of the third toe

Tip of the fourth toe

Tip of the baby toe

Back up to the right ankle joint

Knee joint

Hip joint

Tip of the tailbone

Sweeping awareness to the left hip joint

Left knee joint

Ankle joint

The left big toe

Tip of the second toe

Tip of the third toe

Tip of the fourth toe

Tip of the baby toe

Back up to the left ankle

Knee joint

Hip joint

Tip of the tailbone

Navel centre

Heart centre

Hollow of the throat

The eyebrow centre

The eyebrow centre

The eyebrow centre (pause)

Breath Awareness

Now become aware of the chest.

Notice the body breathing itself.

Chest gently rises and falls with each breath. (pause)

Nothing for you to do.

Simply witnessing. (pause)

Now bring awareness to the nostrils. (pause)

Move awareness to the right nostril.

Feel that with each breath stream coming in the right nostril, heat is created in the body. Each breath coming in the right nostril, heat is created in the body. (pause for a few breaths)

Move awareness to the left nostril.

Feel that with each breath stream coming in the left nostril, cooling is created in the body. Each breath coming in through the left nostril, cooling is created in the body. (pause for a few breaths)

Now bring awareness to both nostrils and feel the balance of two streams of breath coming in, right and left, heating and cooling. Balanced temperature. (pause)

Take a few deep breaths now, fully awake and aware, feeling a balance of heat and cooling in the body. (pause for a few breaths)

Opposites

Now beginning to manifest sensations in the body.

Start by feeling the sensation of a crisp, fall breeze blowing across your whole body.

Feel the cool air blowing, from the tips of your toes to the top of your head, and from the top of your head to the tips of your toes. (pause)

Feel the cool air turning colder.

Feel your whole body naturally contracting, pulling in from the cold – deep in until your body shivers. (pause)

Cold permeating your skin… tissues… deep into your bones.

Goosebumps across your body. Shivering. (pause)

Notice the breath in your left nostril.

Feel cold air flowing in with each inhalation. Feel the contraction in the nostril and the cooling sensation. (pause)

With each breath in through the left nostril, your body becomes colder and colder. (pause)

Goosebumps. Shivering. (pause)

Feel cold in all parts of the body – cold in the arms, cold legs, cold torso, head. Feel the cold on your face – cheeks, tip of your nose, forehead, ears. Cold at your temples, up along the back of your neck, shivering, cold at the top of your head.

Cold, shivering throughout the whole body. (pause)

Now let go of the sensation of cold.

Completely let it go.

Let go of the sensation of cold throughout the whole body. (pause)

Notice that you can release the sensation of cold from your body anytime you need. (pause)

Now manifesting the sensation of heat in the body.

Feel heat arising in the whole body.

Bring awareness to the navel centre.

This is a chakra, or energy centre, where you can create heat and radiate it throughout the body. (pause)

Feel the navel centre like a blazing fire, the intensely hot core of the sun. (pause)

Feel incredible heat, radiating out, creating warmth for your whole body, right out to the tips of your fingers and toes. Heat flowing out, like lava, permeating your whole body. (pause)

Feel heat deep in your bones, radiating out, expanding in all directions, to the muscles, the skin, the arms and legs, tips of the toes and fingers, the face, the ears, the top of the head.

Abundance of heat throughout the whole body. (pause)

So much heat, it spills out, even heating the air surrounding your body. Heat wave. (pause)

Feel heat it in every pore of your body. So much heat, sweat is escaping from your pores. Feel your whole body breaking out in a sweat. Armpits sweating, forehead sweating, eyelids sweating, palms sweating, soles of the feet hot and sweating. Heat throughout the entire body. (pause)

Notice the breath in your right nostril. With each exhalation, notice the expansion of the right nostril and the sensation of heat flowing out from the nostril. (pause)

With each breath through the right nostril, develop the feeling of heat.

Each inhale and exhale through the right nostril, intensify the feeling of heat throughout the whole body. So much heat it is radiating out. Hot, sweating. (pause)

Now let go of the sensation of heat.

Completely let it go.

Let go of the sensation of heat throughout the whole body.

Notice you have the power to manifest or let go of heat in the body, any time you need. (pause)

Take a moment now to rest in the awareness of your power. You have the power to manifest or let go of any temperatures, anytime you like. (pause)

Symbols/Visualization

Now opening the doors of intuitive knowing. Always available to you, effortlessly. (pause)

A series of symbols will be named. Images, thoughts or feelings might arise.

Continue to be the witness. Be effortless.

Simply watching, with detached awareness.

Nothing to do. (pause)

A pen and notebook (repeat 3 times)

Sunrise (repeat 3 times)

Red apples (repeat 3 times)

Beach towel (repeat 3 times)

Stack of papers (repeat 3 times)

Vegetable garden (repeat 3 times)

Snowy mountain (repeat 3 times)

Bowl of rice (repeat 3 times)

A fluffy blanket (repeat 3 times)

Sunshine through the trees (repeat 3 times)

(pause)

Sankalpa

Now is the perfect time to repeat your fall intention. If you repeat it with feeling and awareness now, it cannot fail. Say to yourself mentally,

I shift *beautifully* into the season of *letting go*. (pause)

I shift beautifully into the season of letting go. (pause)

I shift beautifully into the season of letting go. (pause)

Know that your intention has been received deep in your being, and is already manifesting. Take a moment to feel the peace of this intention manifested. (long pause)

Externalization

Become aware of your breath.

Your body resting, breathing itself. (pause)

Hear the sound of your body breathing. (pause)

Feel the sensation of your body breathing. (pause)

Externalizing your awareness.

Become aware of the room you're in, floor, walls, ceiling. (pause)

Listen for sounds within the room. (pause)

Know that the practice of Yoga Nidra is coming to an end.

Develop awareness of your body and the place you're in. (pause)

Feel your awareness coming back into the body.

Yoga Nidra is now complete. (pause)

Beginning gentle movements in the body, wiggle your fingers. Wiggle your toes.

Make any gentle movements with the body that feel good. (pause)

Now make any larger movements – move your feet, legs, hands, arms, move any body parts that are calling you. (pause)

If you're lying down, when you're ready, roll your body to the right side. (pause)

Take a few deep breaths, integrating your Yoga Nidra experience into your everyday experience. (pause)

If you were lying down, press yourself slowly up to sitting. Keep your eyes closed if you can. Take your time, there's no rush. (pause)

Sitting comfortably, back as straight as you can make it.

Take a deep breath in… and a long breath out.

Say to yourself mentally one more time:

"I shift beautifully into the season of letting go." (pause)

Hold that feeling with you. We'll finish by chanting Om and Shanti, three times each.

Om Om Om Shanti Shanti Shanti (pause)

And when you're ready, softly open your eyes. Allow your eyes to adjust to the room. Aware of yourself in the room, and your intention to shift beautifully into the season of letting go.

Shifting Seasons Yoga Nidra – Fall to Winter
(35 min.)

Synchronize with the rhythm of nature and shift beautifully from the season of letting go to the season of deep reflection and rest. Suggested Pre- and Post-Practices:

- Since this Yoga Nidra practice is meant for transitioning to Winter, a Prana Restorative Yoga class, which both rests and energizes would be ideal. (see my Prana Restorative Yoga course at tamaraskyhawk.com for details.)

- Prepare or finish with a meditative mudra such as Chin Mudra or Hakini Mudra.

- Prepare or finish with a Shanti Mantra such as:

  Sarvesham svastir bhavatu

  Sarvesham shantir bhavatu

  Sarvesham purnam bhavatu

  Sarvesham mangalam bhavatu

  (May prosperity be unto all, may peace be unto all, may fullness be unto all, may auspiciousness be unto all)

Settling

Find yourself a comfortable place to lie down, or if you prefer, a place to sit up, supported.

Getting ready for your Yoga Nidra practice focused on shifting beautifully and effortlessly into the season of rest and reflection. (pause)

Have a thin pillow or blanket tucked comfortably under your head.

Cover yourself with a blanket if you like. Do anything you need to do to be comfortable. Deliciously comfortable. (long pause)

Set aside anything that's on your mind. Right now, there's nothing you need to do. Set everything aside for this time to connect within. (pause)

If you're lying in savasana, legs are apart. Feet flopped out to the sides. Arms are away from the body, leaving space beneath the armpits. Palms are facing up.

In any position, shoulders are away from the ears.

Check that your neck is in line and feeling comfortable. (pause)

Check for any lumps or bumps of clothing, jewellery, or the surface beneath you that might draw your attention away.

If you find any, adjust them now. (pause)

Scan your whole body, checking that you're as comfortable as can be and that there's nothing calling your attention – nothing that might draw your attention away from the practice of Yoga Nidra. (pause)

Take a deep breath in… and a long breath out.

Take another deep breath in and as you exhale, feel yourself settle, and let go.

Now is the time to make any final adjustments you need so you can be still for your Yoga Nidra practice. (pause)

Make sure you're completely comfortable and can completely surrender all doing.

Know that you can move whenever you need to, but make yourself so comfortable you'll have absolutely no desire to move. (pause)

Begin to feel that stillness. Rest in that stillness. (pause)

Become aware of distant sounds. (pause)

Allow your sense of hearing to extend out, receiving all sounds effortlessly and without analysis. Simply receiving with effortless awareness. (long pause)

Now bring your hearing into the room. Receiving sounds within the room. (pause)

Hear the sound of your own body breathing. (pause)

Feel the body resting. (pause)

Be aware of your body breathing. (pause)

Your body breathing itself. (pause)

Nothing to do.

No need for concentration. Just effortless awareness. (pause)

Say to yourself mentally, "I'm going to practice Yoga Nidra." (pause) "I will remain awake and aware." (pause)

Yoga Nidra has now begun. (pause)

Sankalpa

With a focus on shifting into the winter season, know that winter is arriving.

Feel that winter is arriving.

All of nature slows in winter. Nothing to do but rest.

Animals are resting, plants are resting, and *you* are resting.

Picture yourself effortlessly following this rhythm of nature. (pause)

Slowing down. Resting for a while.

Without *any* guilt, letting go of the need to do. (pause)

Knowing that it is perfectly natural to *not do* right now.

Embracing the joy of simple rest. Effortless rest. (pause)

See your body being rejuvenated and healed as you rest. (pause)

Rest creates time and space for reflection.

You find yourself naturally falling into reflection and a-ha moments.

Spontaneous moments of reflection.

Without effort.

Beautifully effortless.

Setting a winter intention, say to yourself mentally now,

I shift *beautifully* into the season of *rest* and *reflection*. (pause)

I shift beautifully into the season of rest and reflection. (pause)

I shift beautifully into the season of rest and reflection. (pause)

Rotation of Consciousness

Now taking a trip through the body, witnessing with curiosity and effortless awareness.

Allow the mind to hop from one body part to the next.

No need to think. Just awareness.

Awareness of any sensations, thoughts, feelings that might arise, but without attachment.

Simply noticing and moving freely on.

Bring awareness to the point between the eyebrows

The hollow of the throat

The right shoulder

The right elbow

Effortless travelling deep in the body

Down to the middle of the right wrist

The right thumb

The tip of the index finger

Tip of the middle finger

Tip of the ring finger

Tip of the little finger

Back up to the wrist

The elbow

The shoulder

The hollow of the throat

Sweeping awareness over to the left shoulder

Down to the left elbow

Deep in the body, effortless

The middle of the left wrist

The left thumb

Tip of the index finger

Tip of the middle finger

Tip of the ring finger

Tip of the little finger

Back up to the wrist

The elbow

The shoulder

The hollow of the throat

The heart centre

The right side of the chest

The heart centre

The left side of the chest

The heart centre

The navel centre

Tip of the tailbone

The right hip joint

The right knee joint

The ankle joint

The right big toe

Tip of the second toe

Tip of the third toe

Tip of the fourth toe

Tip of the baby toe

Back up to the right ankle joint

Knee joint

Hip joint

Tip of the tailbone

Sweeping awareness to the left hip joint

Left knee joint

Ankle joint

The left big toe

Tip of the second toe

Tip of the third toe

Tip of the fourth toe

Tip of the baby toe

Back up to the left ankle

Knee joint

Hip joint

Tip of the tailbone

Navel centre

Heart centre

Hollow of the throat

The eyebrow centre

The eyebrow centre

The eyebrow centre

Breath Awareness

Now become aware of the chest.

Notice the body breathing itself. (pause)

Chest gently rises and falls with each breath.

Nothing for you to do.

Simply witnessing.

Awake and aware

Now bring awareness to the nostrils.

Feel the breath in the nostrils. (pause)

Move awareness to the right nostril.

Feel that with each breath stream coming in the right nostril, heat is created in the body. (pause for 3 breaths)

Move awareness to the left nostril.

Feel that with each breath stream coming in the left nostril, cooling is created in the body. (pause for 3 breaths)

Now bring awareness to both nostrils and feel the balance of two streams of breath coming in, right and left, heating and cooling. (pause)

Take a few deep breaths now, fully awake and aware, watching the breath in the nostrils, feeling a balance of heat and cooling in the body. (pause for 3 breaths)

Opposites

Now beginning to manifest sensations in the body.

Start by feeling the sensation of crisp, cold winter air on your face… your arms… hands… legs… feet.

As if you've just stepped outside into a crisp winter's day.

Feel the cold permeating your clothes, from the tips of your toes to the top of your head, and from the top of your head to the tips of your toes. (pause)

Cold air.

Feel your whole body naturally contracting, pulling in from the cold – deep in until your body shivers.

Cold permeating your skin… tissues… deep into your bones.

Goosebumps across your body. Shivering.

Notice the breath in your left nostril.

Feel cold air flowing in with each inhalation. Feel the contraction in the nostril and the cooling sensation.

With each breath in through the left nostril, your body becomes colder and colder. (pause)

Goosebumps. Shivering. (pause)

Feel cold in all parts of the body – cold in the arms, cold legs, cold torso, head. Feel the cold on your face – cheeks, tip of your nose, forehead. Cold at your temples, up along the back of your neck, shivering, cold at the top of your head.

Cold and shivering throughout the whole body. (pause)

Now let go of the sensation of cold.

Completely let it go.

Let go of the sensation of cold throughout the whole body. (pause)

Notice that you can release the sensation of cold from your body anytime you need. (pause)

Now manifesting the sensation of heat in the body.

Feel heat arising in the whole body.

Bring awareness to the navel centre.

This is a chakra, or energy centre, where you can create heat and radiate it throughout the body.

Feel the navel centre like a blazing fire, the intensely hot core of the sun.

Feel incredible heat, radiating out, creating warmth for your whole body, right out to the tips of your fingers and to the tips of your toes. Heat permeating your whole body.

Feel heat deep in your bones, radiating out, expanding in all directions, to the muscles, the skin, the arms and legs, tips of the toes and fingers, the face, the ears, the top of the head.

No shortage of heat, abundance of heat throughout the whole body.

So much so, it spills out, even heating the air surrounding your body. Heat wave. Feel heat it in every pore of your body. So much heat, sweat is trying to escape from your pores. Feel your whole body breaking out in a sweat. Armpits sweating, forehead sweating, eyelids sweating, palms sweating, soles of the feet hot and sweating. Heat throughout the entire body. Hot. Sweating. (pause)

Now let go of the sensation of heat.

Completely let it go.

Let go of the sensation of heat throughout the whole body. (pause)

Notice you have the power to manifest heat in the body any time you need.

Take a moment now to rest in the awareness of your power. You have the power to manifest or let go of any temperatures, anytime you like. (pause)

Symbols/Visualization

Now opening the doors of intuitive knowing. Always available to you, effortlessly.

A series of symbols will be named. Images, thoughts or feelings might arise.

Continue to be the witness. Be effortless.

Simply watching, with detached awareness. (pause)

150

A paperback book (repeat 3 times)

Starry sky (repeat 3 times)

Glistening snow drift (repeat 3 times)

A white sand beach (repeat 3 times)

An old hat (repeat 3 times)

Trees swaying in the wind (repeat 3 times)

A hot bath (repeat 3 times)

Freshly-pressed juice (repeat 3 times)

A fluffy pillow (repeat 3 times)

Sunshine through a window (repeat 3 times)

(pause)

Sankalpa

Now is the perfect time to repeat your winter intention. If you repeat it with feeling and awareness now, it cannot fail. Say to yourself mentally,

I shift *beautifully* into the season of *rest* and *reflection*. (pause)

I shift beautifully into the season of rest and reflection. (pause)

I shift beautifully into the season of rest and reflection. (pause)

Know that your intention has been received deep in your being and is already manifesting. Take a moment now to feel the peace of your intention manifested. (pause for 2 minutes)

Externalization

Become aware of your breath.

Your body resting, breathing itself. (pause)

Hear the sound of your body breathing. (pause)

Feel the sensation of your body breathing. (pause)

Externalizing your awareness.

Become aware of the room you're in, floor, walls, ceiling. (pause)

Listen for sounds within the room. (pause)

Know that the practice of Yoga Nidra is coming to an end.

Develop awareness of your body and the place you're in.

Feel your awareness coming back into the body.

Yoga Nidra is now complete. (pause)

Beginning gentle movements in the body, wiggle your fingers. Wiggle your toes.

Make any gentle movements with the body that feel good. (pause)

Now make any larger movements – move your feet, legs, hands, arms, move any body parts that are calling you. (pause)

And if you're lying down, when you're ready, roll your body to the right side. (pause)

Take a few deep breaths, integrating your Yoga Nidra experience into your everyday experience. (pause for 3 breaths)

If you were lying down, press yourself slowly up to sitting.

Take your time, there's no rush. (pause)

Sitting comfortably, back as straight as you can make it.

Take a deep breath in… and a long breath out.

Say to yourself mentally one more time:

"I shift beautifully into the season of rest and reflection." (pause)

We'll finish by chanting Om and Shanti, three times each.

Om Om Om Shanti Shanti Shanti (pause)

And slowly opening your eyes, adjusting back into the room, back into your day, carrying the sensation of shifting beautifully into the season of rest and reflection.

Self Love Yoga Nidra *(35-40 min.)*

Welcome, discover and appreciate the layers of your being one by one and discover the peace beyond.

Suggested Pre- and Post-Practices:

- Prepare or finish with a few minutes of Samputa Mudra to balance elemental energies, soothe emotions and open up to experience your true nature.

- Prepare or finish with a wholeness mantra such as:

  Om Purnamadah Purnamidam

  Purnat Purnam Udacyate

  Purnasya Purnamadaya

  Purnamaivavashisyate

  Om Shanti Shanti Shanti

(That is whole, this is whole. From that whole this whole arises. From that whole, when this whole is negated, what remains is whole.)

Settling

Getting comfortable – lying on your back or if it's not comfortable, lying on your side, or sitting up, supported.

Maybe making a cozy rest nest with cushions, blankets, bolsters, eye pillow – whatever your body needs to feel as comfortable as possible in this moment. (long pause)

Getting ready to do nothing. (pause)

This time is just for you.

This practice is just for you.

There are no shoulds or shouldn'ts.

There's no way you can do this wrong.

This is about you.

This is for you.

So make yourself as comfortable as you like in just the way you like. (pause)

Adjusting anything you like. In any way you like.

Listening in to what you need. And then answering that request.

You might prefer a lot of cushions, blankets and props, you might prefer just a few, you might even prefer none. All are equally welcome.

Do whatever you need feel supported, held, and free to let go of tensions. (pause)

Getting comfortable for this practice of non-doing.

Check in with how you feel. Your set-up should make you feel at ease, but not sleepy. (pause)

If you do feel sleepy, you could make it slightly less warm, slightly less dark.

You can also check your head position. If your chin is tucked in, it can stimulate sleep. Try moving your head into a neutral alignment, chin neither tucked nor raised, and notice how it might change your energy and alertness. Try moving your head into a position where you feel relaxed yet still alert, not sleepy. (pause)

Set yourself up so you can stay awake and aware, and at the same time, in peaceful ease. (pause)

Beginning a check now that each body part is as relaxed as can be. If you can't completely relax, that's fine. You're welcome just as you are. (pause)

Check that your feet and ankles are relaxed as can be. (pause)

Calves, knees and thighs relaxed as can be. (pause)

154

Hips relaxed as can be. (pause)

Lower back, middle back, upper back releasing tension. Whole back, melting. (pause)

Hands and arms letting go. (pause)

Shoulders and neck melting, tension diffusing. (pause)

Jaw, tongue and cheeks softening. (pause)

Eyes, forehead and scalp softening. (pause)

Whole body, melting into the support of the earth beneath you. Held by the support of the earth beneath you. (pause)

Nothing for you to do. (pause)

Body is supported and resting. (pause)

Awareness continues on. (pause)

Yoga Nidra has now begun. (pause)

Rotation of Consciousness

Now beginning the process of sweeping energy throughout the body.

As awareness moves, you direct energy from point to point.

You might like to experience it as a loving caress of energy. Or a little smile to each body part along the way. (pause)

Experiencing in any way that feels soothing. (pause)

Float awareness over to the right hand

Welcome the right hand thumb

Index finger

Middle finger

Ring finger

Little finger

Awareness floating over to the left hand thumb

All experiences are welcome

Index finger

Middle finger

Ring finger

Little finger

Right wrist

Left wrist

Right elbow

Left elbow

Soothing caress of energy

Right shoulder

Left shoulder

Hollow of the throat

Back of the head near the top

Crown of the head

Eyebrow centre

Right eyebrow

Left eyebrow

Right eye

Left eye

Right ear

Left ear

Right cheek

Left cheek

Tip of the nose

Upper lip

Lower lip

Tip of the chin

Hollow of the throat

Heart centre

Right side of the chest

Heart centre

Left side of the chest

Heart centre

Navel centre

Tip of the tailbone

Right hip

Left hip

Right knee

Left knee

Sweeping energy

Right ankle

Left ankle

Right big toe

Second toe

Third toe

Fourth toe

Little toe

Left big toe

Second toe

Third toe

Fourth toe

Little toe

The whole right side of the body

All is welcome.

The whole left side of the body

All is welcome.

The whole body together

The whole body together

The whole body together (pause)

Welcome the whole body, all at once.

Every aspect of the body, in every way is welcome.

And now, allow the memory of one lovely experience you've had in your life to arise in your awareness. Lovely experience. (pause) Something that made you smile. Maybe something you saw, felt, tasted, smelled. Maybe even just the ease of this moment. (pause)

Thanking the body for its role in allowing you to be there at that moment. To enjoy that lovely experience. (pause)

Thanking your body for all the little ways it's contributed to the joy, learning and evolving in your life. (pause)

Appreciating the body and also knowing, your being extends far beyond the body alone. Exploring further now, beyond the physical body, to the energy body.

Breath Awareness

Bring awareness to the breath. (pause)

Just the natural breath, nothing for you to do. (pause)

Body is miraculously breathing itself. (pause)

Body is taking care of this for you. (pause)

Notice the breath flowing in and out, through the nostrils.

Two streams of air, softly flowing in and flowing out. (pause)

Feel as you breathe in that you are breathing in energy – vital life force. (pause)

This vital life force is known as prana. Breathing in prana, energy. (pause)

As this energy flows in, feel that you pull it in, all the way down to the navel centre.

And as you exhale, feel the energy disperse out, to all parts of the energy body.

Inhale pulling energy in, deep down to the navel centre.

Exhale energy dispersing, through a network of energy tubes, like the nerves of the physical body.

Inhaling energy down to the navel centre.

Exhaling, it disperses out to the tips of the fingers, toes, crown of the head.

Inhale down to the navel centre.

Exhale energy out to all parts of your energy body.

Keep breathing in this way for the next few breaths, inhaling energy, exhaling dispersing energy throughout your energy body. (pause for 30 seconds)

Bring awareness back to the breath if it's wandered off.

Inhaling energy, exhaling dispersing energy throughout the energy body.

Maybe beginning to feel as if the whole body is alive with energy. Pulsing, vibrating, tingling. (pause)

Recognizing this energy body. A more subtle aspect of your being.

The energy body gives life to all aspects of your being and allows you to *feel*.

Noticing any positive sensation in this moment. Maybe a feeling of energy, peace, expansion. Give gratitude to the energy body for allowing you feel this positive sensation. (pause)

Diving further into the self now. Exploring on. There are deeper layers of your being to discover. (pause)

Symbols/Visualization

Now opening up to the creativity of the mind and access to inner wisdom. (pause)

A series of symbols will be named.

The mind might or might not spontaneously project images.

Simply be the witness. As if watching a screen.

Images or no images, it doesn't matter.

Simply watching, with detached awareness. (pause)

A bright star (repeat 3 times)

Paper airplane (repeat 3 times)

Frog in a pond (repeat 3 times)

Yellow flower (repeat 3 times)

Misty mountains (repeat 3 times)

Bushel of apples (repeat 3 times)

Waves on the ocean (repeat 3 times)

Cozy sweater (repeat 3 times)

Pink clouds (repeat 3 times)

Sunlight shining through a crystal (repeat 3 times)

(pause)

Taking a moment now to thank the mind for any pleasant, creative or insightful experiences that might have arisen. (pause)

Your mind is a subtle, and useful part of your being, and yet, still, there is more to your self.

The deepest part of yourself is there through it all.

Aware of every experience.

Ever present.

Present in the experience of the physical body. Present when the body is resting.

Present when experiencing the energy body. And when not experiencing the energy body.

Present in the experience of the mind. And even when the mind is resting, as in deep sleep.

There is a thread that remains. The essence of your being.

It is *awareness*. (pause)

Beyond body, energy, mind, you are *awareness*.

Pure awareness, without any trappings.

Unaffected by any state of body, energy or mind.

Eternally peaceful and free. (pause)

Your essence, is peace.

You are peace.

You are the one you've been looking for all along.

You are the one you've been looking for all along. (pause)

Rest now in the sublime beauty and peace that is you.

You in your deepest essence.

Pure awareness.

Eternally peaceful and free. (pause for 4-10min.)

Externalization

Ommmmmm Ommmmmm Ommmmmm

Bringing awareness back to the breath. Notice your body breathing. Feel your body breathing. (pause)

Take a moment to enjoy the non-doing of your breathing. (pause)

Now take a deep breath in. Feel energy and awareness coming back into the body. (pause)

Yoga Nidra is now complete. (pause)

Take another breath. (pause)

And if you feel like making gentle movements in the body, make them. (pause)

If you feel like making larger movements, make them. (pause)

Listening in and moving when and how you'd like. (pause)

If you like, take a moment to recall your experience. (pause)

What will you take with you from your experience today? (pause)

Reminding yourself once again, *you* are the one you've been looking for all along. (pause)

Make your way to sitting upright.

Keep the eyes closed if you can.

Feel the energy rising upward as you sit. (pause)

Feel the body activating.

The mind activating.

And yet, still remaining relaxed.

Possibly feeling more connected than when you began. (pause)

Maybe more peaceful.

Taking a moment to enjoy any positive experience from your Yoga Nidra practice today. (pause)

Thanking yourself for simply being here. (pause)

Thanking yourself for taking this time for yourself. (pause)

I'll finish by chanting Om and Shanti three times each. Join in if you like, and notice your energy rising with the chant.

Om Om Om Shanti Shanti Shanti (pause)

And slowly opening your eyes, carrying any positive experience from your practice into the rest of your day.

Pranic Healing Yoga Nidra *(35-40 min.)*

Explore deep within the physical and energetic bodies, recognize the sensations or experiences of blocked energy and send energy to those areas for healing on a deep level.

* This is not a substitute for proper medical care with a qualified doctor.

Suggested Pre- and Post-Practices:

- Prepare with asanas or functional movements that move the spine in all ways – forward, back, twisting, to the side and inverted if possible.

- Prepare or finish with a few minutes of Samana Mudra for calming, soothing, and balancing prana and elemental energies.

- Prepare or finish with a prana-giving mantra such as:

  Om Haum Joom Saha

Settling

Lying down comfortably or sitting up, supported.

If you're lying down, place a thin pillow or blanket under your head for support, but not so bulky that your head is out of alignment.

Cover yourself with a blanket if you like.

Do anything you need to do to get comfortable for this Yoga Nidra practice to stimulate healing on an energetic level. (pause)

If you're lying in savasana, legs are apart. Feet flopped out to the sides. Your arms are away from the body, leaving space beneath the armpits. Palms are facing up. (pause)

In any position, shoulders are away from the ears. (pause)

Check that your head is comfortable, straight and in alignment. (pause)

Check that everything is just right. Make any adjustments you need. (pause)

Let your whole body be as comfortable as can be. (pause)

Feel the support of the surface beneath you. Let it hold you as you completely surrender to gravity. (pause)

Letting go into the steady support. (pause)

Take a deep breath in… and as you exhale, let go of anything you think you need to do right now. (pause)

There is nothing you need to do. Nothing you have to think about. Set everything aside. (pause)

Bring all of your attention inward. (pause)

Inhale feeling present in this moment.

Exhale letting go of anything outside of this moment.

Inhale feeling present in this moment.

Exhale letting go of anything outside of right here, right now. (pause)

Become aware of your body. Be aware of your whole body from the top of your head to the tips of your toes and from the tips of your toes to the crown of your head.

Feel stillness in your whole body. (pause)

You can move your body any time you need, but make yourself so comfortable you won't have any desire to move. (pause)

Settle into the comfort.

Absolute comfort.

Stillness.

Effortlessness. (pause)

Awake and aware.

Yoga Nidra has now begun. (pause)

Sankalpa

Bring awareness to your body.

Your whole body.

Feel your whole body all at once. (pause)

Feel as if your whole body is breathing. (pause)

Feel that as the body breathes, there is an exchange of energy, from outside your body to within your body. (pause)

Experience the body as an energy field, giving and receiving energy. (pause)

This energy is known as prana. It is the key to your vitality. And the key to your healing.

In this Yoga Nidra practice, you'll explore deep within the energy body.

Right now, mentally scan your body, physically or energetically and notice any areas that might feel dull, blocked, grey. (pause)

These are areas where prana, energy, is not flowing freely.

State this intention to yourself, mentally, now: "Prana flows freely and heals me". (pause)

Feel that it is true, even in this moment.

"Prana flows freely and heals me." (pause)

Once more, with certainty that this intention is already becoming reality.

"Prana flows freely and heals me." (pause)

Feel that this statement has been internalized and is already working its magic for you, from the inside, out. (pause)

Rotation of Consciousness

Now bringing awareness deep into to the physical body.

Exploring throughout the body, from point to point.

Freely shifting awareness from one body part to the next.

Don't get stuck on any one point.

No need to concentrate, think or analyze.

Simply keep moving awareness swiftly and freely.

Starting with the right side of the body

Become aware of the right hand

Right hand thumb

Index finger

Middle finger

Ring finger

Little finger

Palm of the hand

Back of the hand

Wrist

Lower arm

Elbow

Upper arm

Shoulder

Armpit

Right side of the ribs

Right side of the waist

Hip

Thigh

Knee

Lower leg

Ankle

Heel

Sole of the foot

Top of the foot

Right big toe

Second toe

Third toe

Fourth toe

Fifth toe

Awareness moving freely

Shift to the left side

Become aware of the left hand

Left hand thumb

Index finger

Middle finger

Ring finger

Little finger

Palm of the hand

Back of the hand

Wrist

Lower arm

Elbow

Upper arm

Shoulder

Armpit

Left side of the ribs

Left side of the waist

Hip

Thigh

Knee

Lower leg

Ankle

Heel

Sole of the foot

Top of the foot

Left big toe

Second toe

Third toe

Fourth toe

Fifth toe

Awake and aware

Go to the crown of the head

Crown of the head

Forehead

Right temple

Left temple

Right eyebrow

Left eyebrow

Eyebrow centre

Sweeping awareness

Right eye

Left eye

Right ear

Left ear

Right cheek

Left cheek

Right nostril

Left nostril

Upper lip

Lower lip

Chin

Throat centre

Right collarbone

Left collarbone

Right side of the chest

Left side of the chest

Heart centre

Navel

Lower abdomen

Pelvis

Move to the back of the body

Right buttock

Left buttock

Lower back

Middle back

Upper back

Right shoulder blade

Left shoulder blade

Back of the neck

Back of the head

Crown of the head

Move awareness down to the whole right leg

The whole left leg

Both legs together

The whole torso

The whole right arm

The whole left arm

Neck

Head

The whole front of the body

The whole back of the body

Become aware of the whole body together

The whole body together

The whole body together (long pause)

Feeling the body as a field of energy.

An energetic journey is about to begin.

Several body parts will be named.

Experience them energetically, rather than physically.

Start by bringing awareness to the point between the eyebrows

Energetic awareness of the point between the eyebrows

Effortless.

The hollow of the throat

Exploring deep within, to the centre of the right shoulder joint.

Moving awareness down through the marrow of the arm bone to the elbow joint.

Down through the centre of the lower arm bones to the wrist joint.

Experiencing energetically.

Any experiences are welcome.

The right thumb

The tip of the index finger

Tip of the middle finger

Tip of the ring finger

Tip of the little finger

Any experiences or sensations are welcome.

The wrist joint

Elbow joint

Shoulder joint

Hollow of the throat

Over to the left shoulder joint

Awareness goes deep, through the marrow of the left upper arm bone

Down, to the elbow joint

Down, to the wrist joint

Vibration, light or colour might be experienced

The left thumb

Tip of the index finger

Tip of the middle finger

Tip of the ring finger

Tip of the little finger

Back up to the wrist joint

Elbow joint

Shoulder joint

Hollow of the throat

The heart centre

The right side of the chest

The heart centre

The left side of the chest

The heart centre

The navel centre

Tip of the tailbone

The right hip joint

Down the marrow of the right upper leg bone to the knee joint

Down, to the ankle joint

The right big toe

Tip of the second toe

Tip of the third toe

Tip of the fourth toe

Tip of the baby toe

Back up to the right ankle joint

Knee joint

Hip joint

Tip of the tailbone

Sweeping awareness to the left hip joint

Down the marrow of the left upper leg bone to the knee joint

Down, to the ankle joint

The left big toe

Tip of the second toe

Tip of the third toe

Tip of the fourth toe

Tip of the baby toe

Back up to the left ankle joint

Knee joint

Hip joint

Tip of the tailbone

Experiencing energetically

The navel centre (pause)

The heart centre (pause)

Hollow of the throat (pause)

The eyebrow centre

The eyebrow centre

The eyebrow centre (pause)

Full awareness of the whole energy body.

The whole energy body.

The whole energy body. (pause)

Breath Awareness

Feel as if the whole body is breathing.

The whole body is alive with prana. With vital life force. With energy.

Mentally scan your body, physically or energetically and be aware of any one area that might feel dull, tense, grey, blocked or in any way is not feeling at its best. (long pause)

It's important to choose just one area at a time.

As you bring undivided awareness to this one area you bring energy.

Where awareness goes, prana flows. (pause)

Keep awareness on this part, but allow your awareness to become diffused.

Less focused, more diffused, like a cloud of awareness rather than a point. (pause)

Feel that as your awareness diffuses, the area of tension or dullness also disperses and dissolves. (pause)

Tension, block or dullness, breaking up. Dispersing. (long pause)

Taking deep, relaxed breaths.

Effortless awareness on the body part.

Diffused. Blockage dissolving.

Continue breathing in this way for a few more breaths. (pause for several breaths)

Now if you like, bring your awareness to one more area that needs healing.

If there isn't another area, keep awareness on the first area of focus, or bring awareness to the heart centre. (pause)

Effortless, energetic awareness.

Diffused like a cloud.

Take several deep breaths now, feeling as if your awareness diffuses the tension, dullness or blockage of energy. (pause for several breaths)

Sankalpa

Now diffuse your awareness even more.

Diffuse your awareness to the whole energy body all at once. (pause)

Feel your energy body as a network of pathways, pulling energy in, moving it around and breaking through any blockages. (pause)

Repeat mentally again: "Prana flows freely and heals me". (pause)

Feel that it is true.

"Prana flows freely and heals me." (pause)

Repeating mentally, once more, with certainty.

"Prana flows freely and heals me." (pause)

Know that this statement is now planted in a deep part of your being, where thoughts become realities.

Rest now in the peaceful feeling of prana flowing freely, for the next several minutes. (pause for 2-7 minutes)

Externalization

Ommmmmmmmm

Become aware of the breath.

Be aware that the body is breathing. (pause)

Picture yourself resting, breathing. (pause)

Feel the sensation of your abdomen and chest rising and falling with each breath. (pause)

Feel the sensation of breath through the nostrils. (pause)

Notice the sensation of your body resting, supported by the surface beneath you. (pause)

Notice the texture of any fabric against the skin. (pause)

Be aware of the physical body. (pause)

Externalize your awareness.

Take a deep breath, bringing awareness back into the body. (pause)

Yoga Nidra is now complete. (pause)

Wiggle your fingers and toes.

Stretch or move your body any way you like.

Feel energy begin to flow out to each body part as you move. (pause)

And if you're lying down, when you're ready, roll to your right side.

Take a few deep breaths and mentally repeat once again: "Prana flows freely and heals me." Feel this statement with your whole being. (pause)

If you were lying down, press yourself up to sitting. Keep your eyes closed if you can. Take as much time as you need. (pause)

Sitting up, back as straight as you can make it, top of the head rising toward the ceiling.

Take a few deep breaths in, feeling the energy rising. (pause)

We'll finish by chanting Om and Shanti three times each.

Feel the energy rise within you as you chant.

Om Om Om Shanti Shanti Shanti (pause)

And finally, when you're ready, softly, slowly open your eyes.

Adjusting back into the room, back into your day, refreshed and at peace.

Crystal Beach Yoga Nidra *(35-40 min.)*

Journey to an intriguing private beach and discover the gift it has to offer you.

Suggested Pre- and Post-Practices:

- Finish with a few minutes of Yoni Mudra for balancing energies and redirecting prana back into the body.

- Prepare or finish with a prana-giving mantra such as:

  Om Haum Joom Saha

Settling

Getting ready for your Yoga Nidra practice.

This is your time to rest, connect, discover.

Building yourself a comfortable *rest nest*, whatever that might look like.

Lying on your back in savasana, or maybe lying on your side, or sitting up, supported. Whatever is best for today, give yourself full permission to do that. (pause)

Maybe you have a pillow under your head, a blanket covering you, fuzzy socks – whatever is going to help you feel as comfortable as possible.

Getting as comfortable as possible so you can feel fully supported and free to release tension. (pause)

If you like, cover your eyes with a light eye pillow or scarf.

If you feel any tension in your back while you're resting, place a pillow, rolled blanket or bolster under your knees.

Do all the things you need to do to make yourself sublimely comfortable. (pause)

Check that your legs are comfortable... back comfortable... arms comfortable... shoulders... neck... face... the whole body, as comfortable as can be. (pause)

Make any final adjustments now to feel perfectly at ease. (pause)

Feel your body sinking into the support beneath you.

Body fully supported, effortlessly dropping into a state of peace.

Body effortlessly dropping into a state of non-doing. (pause)

Nothing to do.

Letting go of doing.

Shifting into being. (pause)

Feel your body let go of tensions as you give it this sweet permission to do nothing.

Feel your body sigh ahhhhhh at this opportunity to do nothing. (pause)

Letting go of doing.

Shifting into being. (pause)

This is the opportunity your body has been waiting for.

The opportunity to relax and renew, in a state of complete ease.

Notice the sensation of your body letting go of tension in the shoulders.

The back.... the arms... the legs... the face.

Body completely letting go of tension. (pause)

Body is stilling and at ease.

Effortless awareness of this peaceful state of non-doing. (pause)

Allow your awareness to shift now to the sound of the breath. Listen closely to this soft sound of the body breathing itself. (pause)

Feel the stillness of the body. The body can move anytime you need, but if you don't need, dive into the peace of the stillness. (pause)

The body rests, while the awareness moves and explores.

Awake.

Aware.

Effortless. (pause)

Yoga Nidra has now begun. (pause)

Sankalpa

Now if you'd like to make a sankalpa, a heart-felt resolve, allow it to arise in your awareness.

Allow your sankalpa to arise. (pause)

Vividly see your sankalpa manifested. (pause)

Energetically feel your sankalpa manifested. (pause)

And now, repeat your sankalpa mentally, three times with absolute certainty and feeling. (pause)

Feel with certainty that your sankalpa has been received. (pause)

There's nothing you need to do. Your sankalpa is already being manifested. (pause)

Rotation of Consciousness

Now moving awareness into to the body.

Freely shifting awareness from point to point.

No need to concentrate or analyze.

Simply keep moving awareness swiftly and freely.

Starting by bringing awareness to the right side of the body

Become aware of the right hand

Right hand thumb

Index finger

Middle finger

Ring finger

Little finger

Palm of the hand

Back of the hand

Wrist

Awareness moving freely

Right lower arm

Elbow

Upper arm

Shoulder

Armpit

Right side of the ribs

Right side of the waist

Right hip

Thigh

Knee

Lower leg

Ankle

Heel

Sole of the foot

Top of the foot

Right big toe

Second toe

Third toe

Fourth toe

Fifth toe

Awake and aware

Sweeping awareness to the left side of the body

Become aware of the left hand

Left hand thumb

Index finger

Middle finger

Ring finger

Little finger

Palm of the hand

Back of the hand

Wrist

Moving freely

Left lower arm

Elbow

Upper arm

Shoulder

Armpit

Left side of the ribs

Left side of the waist

Left hip

Thigh

Knee

Lower leg

Ankle

Heel

Sole of the foot

Top of the foot

Left big toe

Second toe

Third toe

Fourth toe

Fifth toe

Sweeping awareness to the crown of the head

Crown of the head

Forehead

Right temple

Left temple

Right eyebrow

Left eyebrow

Eyebrow centre

Right eye

Left eye

Right ear

Left ear

Right cheek

Left cheek

Right nostril

Left nostril

Upper lip

Lower lip

Chin

Throat centre

Right collarbone

Left collarbone

Right side of the chest

Left side of the chest

Heart centre

Navel

Lower abdomen

Pelvis

Sweeping awareness to the back of the body

Right buttock

Left buttock

Lower back

Middle back

Upper back

Right shoulder blade

Left shoulder blade

Back of the neck

Back of the head

Crown of the head

Sweep awareness down to the whole right leg

The whole left leg

Both legs together

The whole torso

The whole right arm

The whole left arm

Neck

Head

The whole front of the body

The whole back of the body

Become aware of the whole body together

The whole body together

The whole body together (long pause)

Maybe noticing here, that as your awareness diffuses to the whole body, your sense of self expands.

Perhaps your awareness expands to a field of being. (pause)

Breath Awareness

Notice this field of being, or the whole body, breathing.

The whole self, breathing. (pause)

Inhaling, pulling in cosmic energy.

Exhaling, releasing tension.

Inhaling energy.

Exhaling fatigue.

And if it feels good, breathing in light – radiant and energizing.

Exhaling anything you need to release, like dark smoke leaving your being.

Inhaling radiant light.

Exhaling anything you need to release, like dark smoke that immediately disappears.

We'll take a minute now to breathe. You can breathe normally, or if it feels good, continue breathing in energizing light, exhaling anything you need to release, like dark smoke that immediately dissolves. (pause for 1 minute)

Symbols/Visualization

Return to breathing normally now.

Just watching the natural breath. (pause)

A journey is about to begin.

While your body is safely and comfortably resting, your awareness is free to explore. (pause)

You can bring your awareness back to the body anytime you like.

You can also allow your awareness to explore if you like.

Your awareness is free to travel anywhere you like, in any way you like.

So if you'd like, allow your awareness to consider a journey to a stunningly beautiful, warm, secluded beach. You are the only one who knows of this beach and the only one who is able to go there. This is your own beautiful beach. Completely private and just for you. (pause)

If you like, allow your awareness to fly out of the room and into the sky now, headed for your private beach. You are completely free as awareness. And can return to the body anytime you like. Fly in any way you like, to your beautiful, warm, private beach now.

Noticing the sights as you fly (pause), sounds (pause), maybe smells (pause) and sensations along the way. (pause)

Noticing you're getting closer to your beach.

You can see it in the distance.

Almost there. (pause)

And now finally, setting foot on your beautiful beach.

Noticing the beach is stunning.

The surroundings… the water… and even the sand itself.

It's breathtaking, and you feel completely at ease here.

The sand, in particular is catching your eye.

It's sparkling.

You look very closely at the grains of sand and notice – they are all crystals.

Amethyst, quartz, jade, citrine…

Crystals in every colour. Shining and sparkling.

You can feel the energy. Everything you need is here for you. Healing energy for every aspect of your being. Powerful healing energy.

Take a few minutes now to rest in this crystal sand.

Simply rest. (pause)

Really nestle in and feel held by these powerful, healing crystals all around you. (pause)

And for the next few minutes, take in anything these beautiful, powerful crystals have to offer you. (pause for 4-10min.)

Sankalpa

Resting in the sand, nestled in.

Resting in sparkling, powerful crystals.

And now, in the comfort of this healing crystal sand, on your beautiful private beach just for you, allow your sankalpa to arise in your awareness.

Allow the feeling of your sankalpa to arise. (pause)

Repeat your sankalpa three times, with feeling and certainty. (pause)

Know that all you need is here, within you.

Your sankalpa is already being manifested.

Preparing to depart from the beach, but before you go, if you like, write your sankalpa in the sand. Write your sankalpa in this sand of powerful crystals. (pause)

As you set off to travel back, see the sankalpa written in the sand one more time. (pause)

Say goodbye to your beach and know you can return again anytime you like. (pause)

Fly off into the blue sky once again, taking the same way back as you did before. Noticing again the same smells... the same sounds... the same sights. (pause)

Noticing you're getting closer to the room again, coming back to your body, peacefully resting.

Closer and closer.

You can see your body now, serenely resting.

Bring awareness back into the body.

Externalization

Bringing awareness back into the body, notice the breath flowing in and out of the nostrils. (pause)

Notice the chest rising and falling with each breath. (pause)

Listen for the sound of the breath. (pause)

Yoga Nidra is now complete. (pause)

Taking a few deep breaths now and notice sensation coming back to the body. (pause)

Wiggle your fingers and toes. Feel the energy back in the body like electrical currents.

Stretch or move your body any way you like. Feel energy begin to flow through each body part as you move. (pause)

And if you're lying down, when you're ready, roll to your right side. Take a few deep breaths and mentally repeat your sankalpa one more time. (pause) Feel it fill your whole being. (pause)

Remember your experience at your beautiful crystal beach. What would you like to take with you from your experience today? (pause)

If you were lying down, press yourself up to sitting.

Keep your eyes closed if you can.

Take as much time as you need. (pause)

Sitting up, back as straight as you can make it, top of the head rising toward the ceiling.

Take a few deep breaths in, feeling the energy rising. (pause)

And finally, when you're ready, softly, slowly open your eyes. Adjusting awareness back into the room, back into your day, refreshed, full of life and in peace. (pause)

Taking in this space around you, with awareness of yourself in it. (pause)

Close your eyes once again and we'll finish by chanting Om and Shanti three times each.

Feel the energy rise within you as you chant.

Om Om Om Shanti Shanti Shanti (pause)

Opening your eyes when you're ready, carrying any positive sensations from your Yoga Nidra experience into the rest of your day.

Floating Leaf Yoga Nidra *(35-40 min.)*

Settle into a sense of ease and receive guidance from your spirit guide on this relaxing journey along a mountain stream.

Suggested Pre- and Post-Practices:

- This script assumes familiarity with the concept of sankalpa. If participants don't yet know about sankalpa, begin by explaining, or better yet, taking them through the Guided Sankalpa Setting (page X).

- Prepare with a few minutes of Hakini Mudra for connection of brain hemispheres and improving intuition.

- Prepare or finish with the universal mantra, Om.

Settling

Getting ready for your Yoga Nidra practice.

Getting ready to lie down comfortably or sit up, supported.

Building yourself a comfortable *rest nest*.

A pillow under your head, blanket covering you, fuzzy socks – whatever is going to help you feel as comfortable as possible so you can fall into a deep relaxation.

If you like, cover your eyes with a light eye pillow or scarf.

If you're lying down and are feeling any tension in your back, place a pillow, rolled blanket or bolster under your knees.

Do all the things you need to do to make yourself sublimely comfortable. (pause)

If you're lying on your back in savasana, legs are apart, arms away from the body, shoulders away from the ears, palms up.

Check that you're comfortable.

Make any adjustments you need. (pause)

Make any final adjustments now to feel perfectly at ease. (pause)

Feel your body sinking into the support beneath you.

Body fully supported, effortlessly dropping into a state of peace.

Body effortlessly dropping into a state of non-doing.

Nothing to do.

Letting go of doing.

Shifting, into being.

Feel your body let go of tensions as you give it this sweet permission to do nothing.

Feel your body sigh ahhhhh at this opportunity to do nothing. (pause)

This is the opportunity your body has been waiting for.

The opportunity to relax and renew. In a state of complete ease.

Notice the sensation of your body letting go of tension in the shoulders.

Letting go of tensions in the back.

The arms. (pause)

The legs. (pause)

The face. (pause)

Completely letting go of tension.

Body is still and at ease.

Free in this delicious state of non-doing.

Allow your awareness to shift now to the sound of the breath.

Listen closely to this soft sound of the body breathing itself.

See your body breathing itself, as if you were watching from above.

Seeing your body resting, in complete stillness and peace while your awareness is awake and ready to begin your Yoga Nidra practice.

The body rests, while the awareness moves and explores.

Awake.

Aware.

Effortless.

Yoga Nidra has now begun. (pause)

Sankalpa

Now is the time to plant the seed of your sankalpa.

Allow your sankalpa to arise in your awareness.

Allow the feeling of your sankalpa to arise. (pause)

Vividly see your sankalpa manifested. (pause)

Energetically *feel* your sankalpa manifested. (pause)

And now, repeat your sankalpa mentally, three times with absolute certainty and feeling. (pause)

Feel with certainty that your sankalpa has been planted.

Know that it has already begun to spring to life. (pause)

Rotation of Consciousness

Now moving awareness deep within the body.

Experiencing energetically rather than physically.

Several locations will be mentioned. They are energetic pathways.

Allow attention to move freely from one to the next. No need to concentrate, just moving awareness.

If sensations or experiences arise, simply take notice and move on.

Begin with effortless awareness of the point between the eyebrows

Effortless awareness of the point between the eyebrows

The hollow of the throat

Shifting freely, unattached

The right shoulder joint

Elbow joint

Wrist joint

The right thumb

The tip of the index finger

Tip of the middle finger

Tip of the ring finger

Tip of the little finger

Experiencing energetically

The wrist joint

Elbow joint

Shoulder joint

Hollow of the throat

Over to the left shoulder joint

Elbow joint

Wrist joint

The left thumb

Tip of the index finger

Tip of the middle finger

Tip of the ring finger

Tip of the little finger

Back up to the wrist joint

Elbow joint

Shoulder joint

Hollow of the throat

The heart centre

The right side of the chest

The heart centre

The left side of the chest

The heart centre

The navel centre

Tip of the tailbone

The right hip joint

Right knee joint

Ankle joint

The right big toe

Tip of the second toe

Tip of the third toe

Tip of the fourth toe

Tip of the baby toe

Back up to the right ankle joint

Knee joint

Hip joint

Tip of the tailbone

Sweeping awareness to the left hip joint

Left knee joint

Ankle joint

The left big toe

Tip of the second toe

Tip of the third toe

Tip of the fourth toe

Tip of the baby toe

Back up to the left ankle joint

Knee joint

Hip joint

Tip of the tailbone

The navel centre

The heart centre

Hollow of the throat

The eyebrow centre

The eyebrow centre

The eyebrow centre (pause)

Breath Awareness

Now become aware of the breath in the nostrils. Just as it is. No need to do anything.

Simply be aware of the breath.

Notice the breath coming in like two streams, through the nostrils.

Feel the streams flowing in along the floor of the nasal passages.

And feel the breath flowing out.

Streams of air flowing in along the floor of the nasal passages.

And streams of air flowing out.

Bring awareness to your right nostril.

Follow the inhalation through your right nostril, and as you exhale, feel it flow out through your left nostril.

Keep awareness on the left nostril as you inhale, and exhale feel the breath flow out through the right nostril.

Mental alternate nostril breathing.

Inhale through the right.

Exhale through the left.

Inhale through the left.

Exhale through the right.

Inhale through the right, count 1.

Exhale through the left, count 2.

Inhale through the left, count 3.

Exhale through the right, count 4.

Keep counting, up to 54.

If you lose track, start again. (pause for 2 minutes)

(After 1 minute, say: "Awake and aware.")

Now let go of the count. It doesn't matter what number you got to or if the mind wandered. Letting go of the count.

Symbols/Visualization

Bring your awareness deep within the body once again.

Feel that the whole body is breathing.

Breath coming in and going out through every pore.

Energy flowing in and out. (pause)

Feel yourself as a pulsing field of energy. (pause)

Shift your awareness so you are seeing your body from above.

See the body peacefully resting.

Your body peacefully resting in the room.

Know that you can bring your awareness back into the body anytime you want, but feel free to explore now, in your astral body. Your energy body.

You can move in any way you want and go anywhere you like in your astral body.

You are completely free. (pause)

Take a moment to enjoy this freedom. Move in any way you like. Travel to anywhere you like.

Know that your body is safe and peaceful and you will return to your body again soon. (pause for 1 minute)

Now pausing your travels for a moment, getting ready to take a journey to an exquisite place.

Feel yourself flying over the land. You can see majestic, emerald green mountains in the distance. (pause)

You fly toward them for some time. (pause)

And as you get closer and are flying over the mountain range, you notice the beauty of the trees. A mix of evergreen and leafy trees. Serene and beautiful. (pause)

There is no one around for miles. Just you and nature. Free in your astral body to move in any way you like. (pause)

You see a stream down in a valley.

You fly to that stream.

Getting closer, you see a leaf, floating effortlessly along the gently moving stream. Wonderfully effortless. (pause)

You shrink to the size of a ladybug and land softly on the leaf. (pause)

You sit down, floating on a wide and shiny green leaf. (pause)

The leaf is warmed by the sunlight, and is truly inviting. (pause)

You lie down, and as you lie down, you see the open blue sky above you, with just a few fluffy white clouds. You notice one cloud in the shape of your favourite animal, and it makes you smile. (pause)

You feel the gentle current of the stream beneath you, ushering you forward, effortlessly.

Your heart swells with a moment of gratitude for this incredible and tranquil floating experience, just for you. (pause)

You lie on your side to take in the view of the shoreline as you float by.

You see many types of foliage and flowers – in the most picturesque colours.

Your leaf gets stuck on a rock for a moment, halting your journey. You push off again and the flow of the stream takes you forward once again.

Your leaf is floating close to the shore now and you look to the water.

This is a very still part of the stream and you are still moving along, but slowly now.

The surface of the water is as smooth as glass. It reflects the rocks and plants along the shoreline crystal clear.

At this moment, the reflection of your spirit guide suddenly appears. (pause)

You look up to see your spirit guide standing on the shoreline. (pause)

You reach for a nearby log and dock your leaf so you can take in this special moment to meet with your spirit guide.

Take a moment now to ask your spirit guide anything you like. You can speak to your spirit guide and receive any guidance. (pause for 1 minute)

Sankalpa

Now tell your spirit guide your sankalpa. Repeat it in the presence of your spirit guide three times now, with full feeling and awareness.

Feel that the sankalpa has been nourished now, deep in your being.

In the presence of your spirit guide, your sankalpa comes forth from deep within you, blossoming out at the heart centre like a radiant flower. (pause)

If you like, you can give the flower to your spirit guide as a gift, as another flower, just the same, blossoms out from your heart centre. (pause)

Thank your spirit guide for their guidance. Your spirit guide is settling down on a smooth rock for meditation. Staying docked on the log, you prepare for meditation too. (long pause)

Bring your awareness deep into the heart centre. Deep into the stillness there.

Go deep, deep within that stillness.

Deep within that silence.

Resting here with full awareness for the next several minutes. (pause 2-7 minutes)

Externalization

Ommmmmmmm

Bring awareness to the heart centre if your mind has wandered off.

It's time to say goodbye to your spirit guide. Your spirit guide has come out of meditation as well.

Say goodbye and thank your spirit guide once again. (pause)

From your log, you take off from your leaf, into the sky.

You fly up from the valley, over the mountain range, back over the land you flew over before.

Returning back to the building your body is in. Back to the room.

You see your body still resting peacefully. Beautifully serene.

You bring your energy body back into the physical body.

Astral body back in the physical body.

Beginning to notice sensations in the physical body.

Notice the chest rising and falling with each breath.

Feel the chest rising and falling with each breath.

Yoga Nidra is now complete. (pause)

Taking a few deep breaths now and notice sensation coming back to the body. (pause)

Wiggle your fingers and toes.

Feel the energy back in the body like electrical currents.

Stretch or move your body any way you like. Feel energy begin to flow through each body part as you move. (pause)

And if you're lying down, when you're ready, roll to your right side.

Take a few deep breaths and mentally repeat your sankalpa one more time. (pause) Feel it fill your whole being. (pause)

Remember your experience on the floating leaf and the guidance from your spirit guide. (pause)

If you were lying down, press yourself up to sitting.

Keep your eyes closed if you can.

Take as much time as you need. (pause)

Sitting up, back as straight as you can make it, top of the head rising toward the ceiling.

Take a few deep breaths in, feeling the energy rising. (pause)

And finally, when you're ready, softly, slowly open your eyes.

Adjusting awareness back into the room, back into your day, refreshed and in peace.

With eyes softly focused, take a few breaths, taking in this space around you, with awareness of yourself in it. (pause)

Close your eyes once again and we'll finish by chanting Om and Shanti three times each.

Feel the energy rise within you as you chant.

Om Om Om Shanti Shanti Shanti (pause)

And slowly opening your eyes again, bringing awareness back into the room and carrying any positive sensations from your practice into your day.

Dancing Vine Yoga Nidra *(40-45 min.)*

Vines reach for the sunlight – exploring, changing course, adapting as needed, perpetually enjoying new experiences and perspectives. Dancing in the light all along the way. Where is the sunlight showing up in your life? Tap into your intuition and start moving in that direction now.

Suggested Pre- and Post-Practices:

- This practice assumes some basic familiarity with the concept of sankalpa. Begin with a brief explanation of sankalpa.

- Begin or finish by holding Abhaya Hridaya Mudra for heart-centred fearlessness.

- Prepare or finish with a Shanti Mantra such as:

    Sarvesham svastir bhavatu

    Sarvesham shantir bhavatu

    Sarvesham purnam bhavatu

    Sarvesham mangalam bhavatu

    (May prosperity be unto all, may peace be unto all, may fullness be unto all, may auspiciousness be unto all)

Settling

Lying down comfortably – on your back, your side or your abdomen. Or sitting up, supported.

Any position is fine. Stretched, curled, it doesn't matter.

Listening to the body and choosing the position that best suits you, right now, for your Yoga Nidra practice. For this practice of fluidly dancing in the light, like a vine. (pause)

Cushioning your head with a pillow or blanket.

Cover yourself with a blanket if you like.

Maybe you'd like to *hug* a bolster or blanket.

Maybe an eye pillow to soothe your eyes.

Just listening in and answering the call. (pause)

What is your body asking for in this moment? What will allow you to feel more free? (pause)

Propping and positioning yourself in any way you'd like right now. (long pause)

During this practice, you can move your body any time you need, but make yourself so comfortable you won't want to move. (pause)

Check that everything is just right. (pause)

Check that your feet are comfortable. (pause)

Legs are comfortable. (pause)

Hips are comfortable. (pause)

The whole back. (pause)

Arms and hands. (pause)

Shoulders. (pause)

Neck. (pause)

Jaw, tongue, forehead. (pause)

The whole body, as comfortable as can be. (pause)

Feel the support of the surface beneath you. Let it hold you completely. (pause)

Settling into the support of the earth, sending down steady, firm roots.

Steady, firm roots to give you the freedom to explore far and wide. (pause)

Deep roots. Held steady by the earth. Unconditionally. (pause)

Take a deep breath in… and as you exhale, let go of anything you think you need to do right now. (pause)

There's nothing you need to do. Nothing you have to think about. Set everything aside. (pause)

Body is settling in. (pause)

Attention is drawing inward. (pause)

Inhale feeling present in this moment.

Exhale letting go of anything outside of this moment.

Inhale feeling present in this moment.

Exhale letting go of anything outside of right here, right now. (pause)

Allow your sense of hearing to extend out, receiving sounds, but without analyzing. Simply receiving objectively. Receiving any sounds. (pause)

The farthest sounds (pause)

Near sounds (pause)

Maybe even the sounds within your own body. The sound of your own breath. (pause)

Become aware of the body. Be aware of your whole body from the top of your head down to the toes and from the toes up to the crown of your head.

Be aware that your body is resting comfortably. (pause)

Feel stillness in your body.

If at any time you need to move, then move.

Otherwise, you're free to settle in to the comfort.

Free to settle in to the roots. (pause)

Free to rest the body. (pause)

In absolute comfort.

Just as you like it.

Just for you.

Effortless. (pause)

Body rests, while awareness is free to roam.

Yoga Nidra has now begun. (pause)

Sankalpa

Now if you'd like, allow the joyful feeling of your sankalpa to arise.

If you don't have a sankalpa, or want to explore like a vine, allow an "I am" statement that fills you with joy to arise.

For example, "I am vibrant", "I am abundant", or "I am free". Whatever *stirs your soul*. No need for thinking, just feeling. Finishing this statement: I am… (long pause)

Did anything arise? Anything light you up?

Don't overthink it. Go with that. That little ray of sunshine is your perfect next move forward.

If nothing came to mind, you can use: "I am vibrant", "I am abundant", or "I am free".

Really feel your sankalpa, picture it – as vividly as you can. (pause)

If the feeling is there, it can't help but be manifested.

State your sankalpa now, 3 times with clarity and feeling. (pause)

Rotation of Consciousness

Now beginning the process of enlivening the body with energy.

Several energetic points will be named.

Allow awareness to move freely from point to point.

Maybe experiencing awareness dancing from point to point, like a soft vine of light or colour.

Awareness dancing like a soft vine of light or colour. (pause)

Start with awareness of the right hand thumb

Energetic awareness of the right hand thumb

Now the left hand thumb

The right wrist

The left wrist

Right elbow

Left elbow

Dancing like a vine of light or colour

Right shoulder

Left shoulder

Hollow of the throat

Back of the head near the top

Crown of the head

Eyebrow centre

Right eyebrow

Left eyebrow

Right eye

Left eye

Right ear

Left ear

Right cheek

Left cheek

Tip of the nose

Upper lip

Lower lip

Tip of the chin

Hollow of the throat

Heart centre

Right side of the chest

Heart centre

Left side of the chest

Heart centre

Navel centre

Tip of the tailbone

Right hip

Left hip

Right knee

Left knee

Dancing energy vine

Right ankle

Left ankle

Right big toe

Left big toe

Now the whole right side of the body

The whole left side of the body

The whole body together

The whole body together

The whole body together (pause)

Welcome the whole body, alive with energy. (pause)

Breath Awareness

Now become aware of the breath.

No need to change the breath in any way, simply bring awareness to the breath.

As you exhale, feel that you let go of any fatigue, stress, tension.

As you inhale, feel that you're pulling in *boundless energy*.

Exhale letting go of fatigue, stress, tension.

Inhale filling up with boundless energy.

Exhale from the crown of the head down to the toes.

Inhale from the toes up to the crown of the head.

Exhale from the crown of the head down to the ankles.

Inhale from the ankles up to the crown of the head.

Exhale from the crown of the head down to the knees.

Inhale from the knees up to the crown of the head.

Exhale from the crown down the spine to the tailbone.

Inhale from the tailbone up the spine to the crown.

Exhale from the crown down the spine to the navel.

Inhale from the navel up the spine to the crown.

Exhale from the crown down the spine to the heart centre.

Inhale from the heart centre up the spine to the crown.

Exhale from the crown down to the throat centre.

Inhale from the throat centre up the spine to the crown.

Exhale from the crown down to the bridge between the nostrils.

Inhale from the bridge between the nostrils up to the crown.

Now to the third eye, exhale down to the bridge between the nostrils.

Inhale from the bridge between the nostrils, up to the third eye.

Back to the crown, exhale down to the bridge between the nostrils.

Inhale from the bridge between the nostrils up to the crown.

Exhale from the crown down the spine to the throat centre.

Inhale from the throat centre up the spine to the crown.

Exhale from the crown down the spine to the heart centre.

Inhale from the heart centre up the spine to the crown.

Exhale from the crown down the spine to the navel.

Inhale from the navel up the spine to the crown.

Exhale from the crown down the spine to the tailbone.

Inhale from the tailbone up the spine to the crown.

Exhale from the crown of the head down to the knees.

Inhale from the knees up to the crown of the head.

Exhale from the crown of the head down to the ankles.

Inhale from the ankles up to the crown of the head.

Exhale from the crown of head down to the toes.

Inhale from the toes up to the crown of the head. (pause)

Feel that the whole body is breathing in and out. (pause)

Inhaling cosmic energy from all around you, exhaling any energy blocks. (pause)

Continue to breathe this way for a few breaths.

Inhaling cosmic energy, exhaling any energy blocks. (pause for 3 breaths)

Symbols/Visualization

Shifting to inner wisdom now.

Effortlessly tapping in.

There is an infinite well of knowledge within you. (pause)

A series of symbols will be named.

The mind might or might not spontaneously project images.

There's nothing for you to manifest, search for or think about.

Nothing to do, at all. (pause)

Simply be the witness. As if watching clouds in the sky.

Images or no images, it doesn't matter.

Watching, with detached awareness. (pause)

A bright red chair (repeat 3 times)

Flowing stream (repeat 3 times)

Gift box (repeat 3 times)

Tall trees (repeat 3 times)

Resting lion (repeat 3 times)

Microphone (repeat 3 times)

String of lights (repeat 3 times)

Birthday cake (repeat 3 times)

Tropical beach (repeat 3 times)

Hot air balloon (repeat 3 times)

(pause)

If any insights spontaneously occurred to you, take them with you. If not, that's also fine. Know this time has been useful in awakening your creativity and intuition. (pause)

Now bring awareness to the heart centre.

Effortless awareness of the heart centre. (pause)

Picture at your heart centre a beautiful glowing light.

Beautiful and radiant, like the sun. (pause)

Feel its warmth and light nourishing your whole being. (pause)

This is the heart of your being. Your luminous soul. (pause)

Your soul holds all the answers for you.

As the observer of this beautiful light, you can ask for any guidance you like. Perhaps asking about your next move forward, or anything else that arises.

Take some time now to communicate with your soul. (pause for 1 minute)

And now, thanking your soul for any guidance. (long pause)

Visualizing the soul as radiant light at your heart centre

Allow your awareness to completely absorb into this light.

Absorbing into your soul.

Duality of you as the observer and your soul as the other, dissolves.

Duality dissolves.

There is only you, the Soul that remains.

All thinking ends.

For the next several minutes, resting as the luminous Soul itself. (pause for 5-10 minutes)

Sankalpa

Bringing awareness back to the heart centre.

Effortless awareness of the heart centre. (pause)

If you like, taking the opportunity to allow your sankalpa to arise, your heart-felt resolve. If you don't have a sankalpa, you might have used: "I am vibrant", "I am abundant", or "I am free".

If you repeat your sankalpa with feeling and awareness now, it cannot fail. Say it to yourself mentally, 3 times now. (pause)

Know that your sankalpa has been received deep in your being and is already manifesting. (pause)

Externalization

Now becoming aware of your breath. (pause)

Your body resting, breathing itself. (pause)

Hear the sound of your body breathing. (pause)

Feel the sensation of your body breathing. (pause)

Externalizing your awareness.

Become aware of the room you're in, floor, walls, ceiling. Listen for sounds within the room. (pause)

Know that the practice of Yoga Nidra is coming to an end.

Develop awareness of your body and the place you're in.

Take a deep breath and feel awareness coming back into the body.

Yoga Nidra is now complete. (pause)

Beginning gentle movements in the body, wiggle your fingers. Wiggle your toes.

Make any gentle movements with the body that feel good. (pause)

209

Now make any larger movements – move your feet, legs, hands, arms, move any body parts that are calling you, and if you're lying down, when you're ready, roll to the right side.

Take a few deep breaths, recalling any guidance from your soul or insights from your Yoga Nidra practice today. (pause)

If you were lying down, press yourself slowly up to sitting. Keep your eyes closed if you can. Take your time, there's no rush. (pause)

Sitting comfortably, back as straight as you can make it.

Take a deep breath in… and a long breath out.

Hold the feeling of the dancing vine, moving toward your next ray of sunshine. (pause)

We'll finish by chanting Om and Shanti, three times each.

Om Om Om Shanti Shanti Shanti (pause)

And when you're ready, softly, slowly open your eyes adjusting awareness back into the room. Carrying with you any new insights or positive feelings from your practice today.

Journey Through the Self to the Self Yoga Nidra *(45-55 min.)*

Take a journey through all aspects of yourself from the most tangible to the most subtle, finally resting in the blissful, pure source – the true Self.

Suggested Pre- and Post-Practices:

- This script is not for beginners to Yoga or Yoga Nidra. It's meant for people who have some familiarity with the deeper Yogic concepts of chakras and non-duality (Vedanta philosophy).

- When exploring the chakras, two options are given – silence or chanting bija mantras. I've included the bija mantras because in my experience, it has helped students with awareness of the chakras, but if you're not confident with chanting or the correct pronunciations of the mantras, you can simply hold silence.

- Begin with a mantra that speaks to the nature of the Self, for example:

> Asato Ma Sat Gamaya
>
> Tamaso Ma Jyotir Gamaya
>
> Mrityor Ma Amritam Gamaya
>
> Om Shanti Shanti Shanti (pause)

(Lead me from the unreal to the real, darkness to light, death to immortality)

- Begin with a few minutes of chanting Om while holding Chin Mudra, to connect the individual sense of "I" with pure consciousness.

- Be sure to leave a good amount of time after this session for practitioners to sit with the experience and transition back into their day. No Yoga Nidra should be rushed, but especially one such as this that connects people to their most subtle reality.

Settling

Find a comfortable space to lie down, or if you prefer, a place to sit up, supported.

Getting ready for your Yoga Nidra practice.

We're going to take a journey of discovery – through the layers of your being, to arrive at your true Self. (pause)

Tuck a pillow comfortably under your head.

Maybe a rolled blanket or bolster under your knees if you want to relieve any tension from your lower back

Cover yourself with a blanket if you like.

Making a comfortable rest nest. (long pause)

If you're lying in savasana, legs are apart. Feet flopped out to the sides. Your arms are away from the body, leaving space beneath the armpits. Palms are facing up. (pause)

In any position, shoulders are away from the ears. (pause)

Check that your neck is in line and feeling comfortable and supported. (pause)

Check for any lumps or bumps of clothing, jewellery, or in the surface beneath you that might draw your attention away. If you find any, adjust them now. (pause)

Remember you are about to practice Yoga Nidra, sleep with trace awareness.

Scan your whole body, checking that you are as comfortable as can be and that there's nothing that's drawing your attention away. (pause)

Take a deep breath in... and a long breath out.

Once again take a deep breath in... and as you exhale, feel that you settle, and let go. (pause)

Now is the time to make any final adjustments you need. Know that you can move anytime you like, but if it feels good, enjoy the stillness.

Sink into the stillness.

All you need to do is maintain awareness of hearing. Nothing else to do.

The body relaxes completely, while you remain awake and aware.

Take a deep breath in... and as you breathe out, feel yourself letting go of any worries or tensions.

Once again, deep, soothing breath in...

And exhale letting go.

Now extend your awareness out as far as you can, listening for distant sounds, outside the building (long pause)

Allow your sense of hearing to extend out like a microphone, picking up any sounds without analysis, without thinking. Simply receiving.

Be aware of sounds far in the distance, the furthest sounds you can hear.

Allow awareness to effortlessly, freely move from one sound to the next...

Without analyzing, just receiving. (pause)

Now moving your awareness in closer, to the sounds within the room.

Receiving sounds within the room. (pause)

Now bring awareness to the closest sound – the sound of your body breathing.

Effortless awareness of the sound of your body breathing itself. (pause)

Be aware that you're about to practice Yoga Nidra.

Say to yourself mentally: "I will remain awake and aware." (pause)

Yoga Nidra has now begun. (pause)

Rotation of Consciousness

Bring awareness to the most tangible aspect of yourself – the physical body.

Taking a journey through the body, from point to point.

Freely shifting awareness from one body part to the next.

Don't get stuck on any one point.

No need to concentrate, think or analyze.

Simply keep moving awareness swiftly and freely.

Starting with the right side of the body

Become aware of the right hand

Right hand thumb

Index finger

Middle finger

Ring finger

Little finger

Palm of the hand

Back of the hand

Wrist

Lower arm

Elbow

Upper arm

Shoulder

Armpit

Right side of the ribs

Right side of the waist

Hip

Thigh

Knee

Lower leg

Ankle

Heel

Sole of the foot

Top of the foot

Right big toe

Second toe

Third toe

Fourth toe

Fifth toe

Awareness moving freely

Shift to the left side

Become aware of the left hand

Left hand thumb

Index finger

Middle finger

Ring finger

Little finger

Palm of the hand

Back of the hand

Wrist

Lower arm

Elbow

Upper arm

Shoulder

Armpit

Left side of the ribs

Left side of the waist

Hip

Thigh

Knee

Lower leg

Ankle

Heel

Sole of the foot

Top of the foot

Left big toe

Second toe

Third toe

Fourth toe

Fifth toe

Awake and aware

Go to the crown of the head

Crown of the head

Forehead

Right temple

Left temple

Right eyebrow

Left eyebrow

Eyebrow centre

Sweeping awareness

Right eye

Left eye

Right ear

Left ear

Right cheek

Left cheek

Right nostril

Left nostril

Upper lip

Lower lip

Chin

Throat centre

Right collarbone

Left collarbone

Right side of the chest

Left side of the chest

Heart centre

Navel

Lower abdomen

Pelvis

Move to the back of the body

Right buttock

Left buttock

Lower back

Middle back

Upper back

Right shoulder blade

Left shoulder blade

Back of the neck

Back of the head

Crown of the head

Move awareness down to the whole right leg

The whole left leg

Both legs together

The whole torso

The whole right arm

The whole left arm

Both arms together

Neck

Head

The whole front of the body

The whole back of the body

Become aware of the whole body together

The whole body together

The whole body together (long pause)

You are now more deeply aware of your body.

You are aware of the body.

YOU are aware of the body.

Notice there are two parts in that statement – *you* and the body.

"YOU" is something separate from the body.

"YOU" are not the body.

Say to yourself mentally,

I am not the body. (pause)

I am not the body. (pause)

I am not the body. (pause)

Resist the temptation to let the mind wander off thinking.

Simply continue to stay relaxed, effortless.

The aspects of yourself will reveal themselves one by one in this journey.

There's nothing you need to do.

Breath Awareness

Continuing to explore on.

Awake and aware.

Now taking a journey to discover a subtler aspect of yourself – the energy body.

Becoming aware of the energy body by becoming aware of the chakras, or energy centres.

Keep your awareness keen yet relaxed.

You might notice pulsation, light, colour or other experiences as you locate the energy centres.

This is fine.

You might NOT notice pulsation, light, colour as you locate the energy centres.

This is also fine.

There's no goal. Simply stay awake and aware.

The first energy centre is the root chakra.

Find it at the perineum or just below the tailbone. (pause)

> Perineum or just below the tailbone. (pause)

> Breathe deeply as if you are pulling energy in through the nostrils and down to this root centre.

219

(pause for 3 breaths or…)

Feel the vibration of this mantra at the root chakra…

LAM… LAM… LAM

The second energy centre is the sacral chakra.

Find it in the sacrum, or lower abdomen. (pause)

Sacrum, or lower abdomen. (pause)

Breathe deeply as if you are pulling energy in through the nostrils and down to this sacral centre.

(pause for 3 breaths or…)

Feel the vibration of this mantra at the sacral chakra…

VAM… VAM… VAM

The third centre is the navel chakra.

Find it in the spinal cord, behind the navel. (pause)

Spinal cord, behind the navel. (pause)

Breathe deeply as if you are pulling energy in through the nostrils and down to the navel centre.

(pause for 3 breaths or…)

Feel the vibration of this mantra at the navel chakra…

RAM… RAM… RAM

The fourth centre is the heart chakra.

Find it in the spinal cord, directly behind the sternum. (pause)

Spinal cord, directly behind the sternum. (pause)

Breathe deeply as if you are pulling energy in through the nostrils and down to the heart centre.

(pause for 3 breaths or…)

Feel the vibration of this mantra at the heart chakra…

YAM… YAM… YAM

The fifth centre is the throat chakra.

Find it at the base of the throat. (pause)

Base of the throat. (pause)

Breathe deeply as if you are pulling energy in through the nostrils and down to the throat centre.

(pause for 3 breaths or…)

Feel the vibration of this mantra at the throat chakra…

HAM… HAM… HAM

The sixth centre is the third eye chakra.

Find it in the centre of the brain behind the point between the eyebrows. (pause)

Centre of the brain, behind the point between the eyebrows. (pause)

Breathe deeply as if you are pulling energy in and out through the third eye centre.

(pause for 3 breaths or…)

Feel the vibration of OM at the third eye…

OM… OM… OM

The last centre is the crown chakra.

Find it at the crown of the head. (pause)

Crown of the head. (pause)

Visualizing a lotus flower of a thousand petals at the crown chakra. Luminous and infinite. Breathe deeply, observing silence. (pause for 3 breaths)

You are now aware of this subtler aspect of yourself – the energy body.

You are aware of the energy body.

YOU are aware of the energy body.

Notice there are two parts in that statement – you and the energy body.

"YOU" is something separate from the energy body.

"YOU" are not the energy body.

Say to yourself mentally,

I am not the energy body. (pause)

I am not the energy body. (pause)

I am not the energy body. (pause)

Resist the temptation to let the mind wander off thinking.

Simply stay relaxed, awake and aware.

The aspects of yourself will reveal themselves one by one in this journey.

There's nothing you need to do.

Opposites

Continuing to explore on.

Beginning the process of manifesting sensations in the body.

Start by developing the feeling of heaviness in the body.

Manifesting heaviness in the body.

Each part of your body becoming heavier and heavier.

Heavy, like lead.

Feel the right leg heavy like lead, sinking into the surface beneath you. So heavy you couldn't even lift it.

Now shift awareness to the left leg.

Develop the sensation of heaviness in the left leg. Left leg becoming heavier and heavier. Sinking down… so heavy you couldn't lift it.

Now feel heaviness in the hips… back… chest… The whole torso is sinking into the surface beneath you. So heavy.

Shoulders now sinking, very heavy. Heaviness extending down the arms and to the hands. Hands heavy, like lead.

Back of the neck, back of the head, heavy and sinking down into the surface beneath you.

Manifesting the sensation of heaviness in the whole body.

Entire body heavy, like lead. (pause)

Now let go of the sensation of heaviness.

Completely let it go.

Release the sensation of heaviness from every part of the body. (pause)

Now awaken the sensation of lightness in the body.

Feel that every part of the body is filling up with lightness, like a helium balloon.

Manifest the feeling of lightness.

Body becoming lighter and lighter.

The right leg becoming light, lifting up.

Left leg filling up with lightness and floating right up.

The right arm becoming lighter and lighter, picking up.

The left arm becoming light, floating up.

The hips and torso becoming light, filling up like a helium balloon, and floating right up.

And finally the head, filling with the sensation of lightness, floating right up.

Entire body, floating up. Light as air.

Experience lightness throughout the entire body.

Absolute lightness. (pause)

Now let go of the sensation of lightness.

Allow your body to gently release the feeling of floating.

Completely let go of the sensation of lightness. (pause)

Now noticing something.

External forces didn't create the sensations of heaviness and lightness.

The mind created them.

You are now aware that the mind can manifest or release sensation in the body.

You are aware of the power of the mind.

You are aware of the mind.

YOU are aware of the mind.

Notice there are two parts in that statement – you and the mind.

"YOU" is something separate from the mind.

"YOU" are not the mind.

Say to yourself mentally,

I am not the mind. (pause)

I am not the mind. (pause)

I am not the mind. (pause)

Resist the temptation to let the mind wander off thinking.

Simply stay relaxed, awake and aware.

The aspects of yourself will reveal themselves one by one in this journey.

Effortlessly.

There's nothing you need to do.

Symbols/Visualization

Continuing to explore on.

You began this journey with awareness of the body.

Then moved your attention to the energy body.

Shifted awareness to the mind.

And now, exploring a part of yourself that is even subtler.

In deep sleep, you enter into this state.

In deep sleep you have no of awareness of your body.

All thinking, all dreaming ends.

Time and space cease to exist. (pause)

You begin to experience the bliss sheath – the subtlest aspect of yourself. (pause)

Right now, allow the awareness of the body, energy body and mind to dissolve.

In their absence, allow sublime peace to arise. (pause)

Awareness of body, energy body and mind dissolving.

Sublime peace arising.

Try to remain awake.

Beyond this peace is the source of your being. The true Self.

Formless.

Without qualities.

Limitless.

Infinite.

Eternal.

Your true nature – here all along.

The one present through all experience – physical, mental and spiritual. Present in waking, dreaming and deep sleep. And yet blissfully unaffected by any.

Ever-present. The witness. Awareness. Pure consciousness.

Allowing any remaining "I"ness to absorb into the self.

Rest in this bliss of your true Self for the next several minutes. (pause for 3-10 min.)

Externalization

Ommmmmmmmm

Become aware of the natural breath.

Awareness of the breath. (pause)

Observe the chest rising and falling with each inhalation and exhalation. (pause)

Notice the gentle contraction of the nostrils on inhalation, expansion on exhalation. (pause)

Bring awareness back into the experience of the physical body. (pause)

Bringing awareness back to the body, the mind, the energy body.

But keeping the realization that you were never a body, a mind or an energy body. You are so much more.

You are infinitely more.

You are infinite awareness.

Pure consciousness.

Ever blissful at your core. (pause)

Know that the practice of Yoga Nidra is coming to an end.

Externalize the mind.

Be aware that your body is resting, practicing Yoga Nidra.

Be aware that you are resting in a room. (pause)

While keeping your eyes closed, mentally visualize the room you're in.

See the walls. The floor. The objects in the room – their placement, colour, textures.

Externalize your awareness. (pause)

Without moving, become aware of the sensations of the physical body – the feel of the body on the surface beneath you. (pause)

The feel of the fabric on your skin. (pause)

The temperature of the air touching your skin. (pause)

Externalize your awareness.

Yoga Nidra is now complete. (pause)

Bringing awareness back into the body, wiggle your fingers, wiggle your toes. Make any gentle movements with the body that feel good (pause)

Now make any larger movements – move your feet, legs, hands, arms, move any body parts that are calling you. (pause)

If you're lying down, when you're ready, roll to the right side.

Take a few deep breaths, integrating your Yoga Nidra experience into your everyday experience. (pause)

Remember what you experienced in this journey. What you came to know. Repeat to yourself one more time:

I am not the body. (pause)

I am not the energy body. (pause)

I am not the mind. (pause)

If you were lying down, press yourself slowly up to sitting. Take your time, there's no rush. (pause)

Sitting comfortably, back as straight as you can make it. Keep your eyes closed if you can.

Take a deep breath in… and a long breath out.

Once you're sitting, softly open your eyes.

Allow your eyes to adjust to the room. (pause)

Aware of yourself in the room.

Closing your eyes again, we'll finish by chanting Om and Shanti, three times each.

Om Om Om Shanti Shanti Shanti (pause)

And when you're ready, slowly open your eyes again, taking your time to adjust back into the room, back into your day. Carrying any positive insights, feelings or sensations with you.

Free Gift!

You are a lovely human being for sharing Yoga Nidra.

I'd like to give you something to enjoy for *your own* practice.

3 Free Audio Recordings

Let me lull you into sweet relaxation, rejuvenation and reconnection with some of my most popular Yoga Nidra practices:

- Anytime Calming
- Overflowing Heart Yoga Nidra
- Rainbow Light Yoga Nidra

Get them at

tamaraskyhawk.com/free now!

Reviews Appreciated!

Enjoy the book?
Sharing a review on Amazon is incredibly helpful in spreading the
goodness. Help more people learn about the book and benefit.

Leave your review on Amazon now!

With much gratitude,
Tamara